MW00630480

Eureka Math
Algebra I
Modules 4 & 5

Special thanks go to the Gordon A. Cain Center and to the Department of Mathematics at Louisiana State University for their support in the development of *Eureka Math*.

For a free *Eureka Math* Teacher Resource Pack, Parent Tip Sheets, and more please visit www.Eureka.tools

Lesson 1: Multiplying and Factoring Polynomial Expressions

Classwork

Opening Exercise

Write expressions for the areas of the two rectangles in the figures given below.

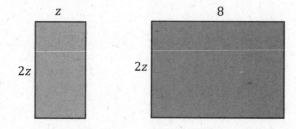

Now write an expression for the area of this rectangle:

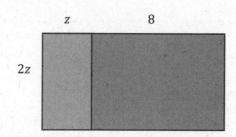

Example 1

Jackson has given his friend a challenge:

The area of a rectangle, in square units, is represented by $3a^2 + 3a$ for some real number a. Find the length and width of the rectangle.

How many possible answers are there for Jackson's challenge to his friend? List the answer(s) you find.

$3a^2 + 3a$ square units

Exercises 1–3

Factor each by factoring out the greatest common factor:

1. $10ab + 5a$

2. $3g^3h - 9g^2h + 12h$

3. $6x^2y^3 + 9xy^4 + 18y^5$

Discussion: The Language of Polynomials

PRIME NUMBER: A *prime number* is a positive integer greater than 1 whose only positive integer factors are 1 and itself.

COMPOSITE NUMBER: A *composite number* is a positive integer greater than 1 that is not a prime number.

A composite number can be written as the product of positive integers with at least one factor that is not 1 or itself.

For example, the prime number 7 has only 1 and 7 as its factors. The composite number 6 has factors of 1, 2, 3, and 6; it could be written as the product $2 \cdot 3$.

A nonzero polynomial expression with integer coefficients is said to be prime or irreducible over the integers if it satisfies two conditions:

(1) It is not equivalent to 1 or -1, and

(2) If the polynomial is written as a product of two polynomial factors, each with integer coefficients, then one of the two factors must be 1 or -1.

Given a polynomial in standard form with integer coefficients, let c be the greatest common factor of all of the coefficients. The polynomial is *factored completely over the integers* when it is written as a product of c and one or more prime polynomial factors, each with integer coefficients.

EUREKA
MATH™

Example 2: Multiply Two Binomials

Using a Table as an Aid

You have seen the geometric area model used in previous examples to demonstrate the multiplication of polynomial expressions for which each expression was known to represent a measurement of length.

Without a context such as length, we cannot be certain that a polynomial expression represents a positive quantity. Therefore, an area model is not directly applicable to all polynomial multiplication problems. However, a table can be used in a similar fashion to identify each partial product as we multiply polynomial expressions. The table serves to remind us of the area model even though it does not represent area.

For example, fill in the table to identify the partial products of $(x + 2)(x + 5)$. Then, write the product of $(x + 2)(x + 5)$ in standard form.

	x	$+$	5
x			
$+$ 2			

Without the Aid of a Table

Regardless of whether or not we make use of a table as an aid, the multiplying of two binomials is an application of the distributive property. Both terms of the first binomial distribute over the second binomial. Try it with $(x + y)(x - 5)$. In the example below, the colored arrows match each step of the distribution with the resulting partial product.

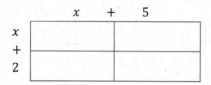

Multiply: $(x + y)(x - 5)$

$$\left.\begin{array}{r} x^2 \\ -5x \\ +yx \\ -5y \end{array}\right\} x^2 - 5x + yx - 5y$$

Example 3: The Difference of Squares

Find the product of $(x + 2)(x - 2)$. Use the distributive property to distribute the first binomial over the second.

<u>With the Use of a Table</u>:

	x	$+$	2
x	x^2		$2x$
$+$			
-2	$-2x$		-4

$x^2 - 4$

<u>Without the Use of a Table</u>:

$(x)(x) + (x)(-2) + (2)(x) + (2)(-2) = x^2 - 2x + 2x - 4 = x^2 - 4$

Exercise 4

Factor the following examples of the difference of perfect squares.

a. $t^2 - 25$

b. $4x^2 - 9$

c. $16h^2 - 36k^2$

d. $4 - b^2$

e. $x^4 - 4$

f. $x^6 - 25$

Write a General Rule for Finding the Difference of Squares

Write $a^2 - b^2$ in factored form.

Exercises 5–7

Factor each of the following differences of squares completely:

5. $9y^2 - 100z^2$

6. $a^4 - b^6$

7. $r^4 - 16s^4$ (Hint: This one factors twice.)

Example 4: The Square of a Binomial

To square a binomial, such as $(x + 3)^2$, multiply the binomial by itself.

$$(x + 3)(x + 3) = (x)(x) + (x)(3) + (3)(x) + (3)(3)$$
$$= x^2 + 3x + 3x + 9$$
$$= x^2 + 6x + 9$$

Square the following general examples to determine the general rule for squaring a binomial:

a. $(a + b)^2$

b. $(a - b)^2$

Exercises 8–9

Square the binomial.

8. $(a + 6)^2$

9. $(5 - w)^2$

Lesson 1:   Multiplying and Factoring Polynomial Expressions

EUREKA MATH

Lesson Summary

Factoring is the reverse process of multiplication. When factoring, it is always helpful to look for a GCF that can be pulled out of the polynomial expression. For example, $3ab - 6a$ can be factored as $3a(b - 2)$.

Factor the difference of perfect squares $a^2 - b^2$:

$$(a - b)(a + b).$$

When squaring a binomial $(a + b)$,

$$(a + b)^2 = a^2 + 2ab + b^2.$$

When squaring a binomial $(a - b)$,

$$(a - b)^2 = a^2 - 2ab + b^2.$$

Problem Set

1. For each of the following, factor out the greatest common factor:

   a. $6y^2 + 18$

   b. $27y^2 + 18y$

   c. $21b - 15a$

   d. $14c^2 + 2c$

   e. $3x^2 - 27$

2. Multiply.

   a. $(n - 5)(n + 5)$

   b. $(4 - y)(4 + y)$

   c. $(k + 10)^2$

   d. $(4 + b)^2$

3. The measure of a side of a square is x units. A new square is formed with each side 6 units longer than the original square's side. Write an expression to represent the area of the new square. (Hint: Draw the new square and count the squares and rectangles.)

   Original Square x

---

4. In the accompanying diagram, the width of the inner rectangle is represented by $x - 3$ and the length by $x + 3$. The width of the outer rectangle is represented by $3x - 4$ and the length by $3x + 4$.

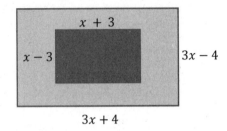

a. Write an expression to represent the area of the larger rectangle.

b. Write an expression to represent the area of the smaller rectangle.

c. Express the area of the region inside the larger rectangle but outside the smaller rectangle as a polynomial in terms of x. (Hint: You will have to add or subtract polynomials to get your final answer.)

©2015 Great Minds eureka-math.org
ALG I-M4-SE-B2-1.3.1-10.2015

Lesson 2: Multiplying and Factoring Polynomial Expressions

Classwork

Example 1: Using a Table as an Aid

Use a table to assist in multiplying $(x + 7)(x + 3)$.

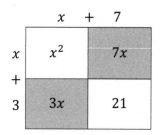

$$x^2 + 10x + 21$$

Exercise 1

1. Use a table to aid in finding the product of $(2x + 1)(x + 4)$.

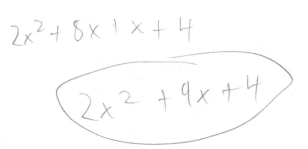

$$2x^2 + 8x \; 1 \; x + 4$$

$$2x^2 + 9x + 4$$

POLYNOMIAL EXPRESSION: A *polynomial expression* is either:

(1) A numerical expression or a variable symbol, or

(2) The result of placing two previously generated polynomial expressions into the blanks of the addition operator (__+__) or the multiplication operator (__×__).

Exercises 2–6

Multiply the following binomials; note that every binomial given in the problems below is a polynomial in one variable, x, with a degree of one. Write the answers in standard form, which in this case takes the form $ax^2 + bx + c$, where a, b, and c are constants.

2. $(x + 1)(x - 7)$

$$x^2 - 7x + x - 7$$
$$x^2 - 6x - 7$$

3. $(x + 9)(x + 2)$

$$x^2 + 2x + 9x + 18$$
$$x^2 + 11x + 18$$

4. $(x - 5)(x - 3)$

$$x^2 - 8x + 15$$

$$x^2 - 6\tfrac{1}{2}x - \tfrac{15}{2}$$

5. $\left(x + \frac{15}{2}\right)(x - 1)$

$$x^2 - x + \frac{15}{2}x - \frac{15}{2}$$
$$x^2 - x + 7\tfrac{1}{2}x - \frac{15}{2}$$

6. $\left(x - \frac{5}{4}\right)\left(x - \frac{3}{4}\right)$

Describe any patterns you noticed as you worked.

Lesson 2:   Multiplying and Factoring Polynomial Expressions

EUREKA MATH™

Exercises 7–10

Factor the following quadratic expressions.

7. $x^2 + 8x + 7$

$$(x+1)(x+1)$$

8. $m^2 + m - 90$

$$(m-9)(m+10)$$

9. $k^2 - 13k + 40$

$$(k-5)(k-8)$$

10. $v^2 + 99v - 100$

$$(v+100)(v-1)$$

Example 3: Quadratic Expressions

If the leading coefficient for a quadratic expression is not 1, the first step in factoring should be to see if all the terms in the expanded form have a common factor. Then, after factoring out the greatest common factor, it may be possible to factor again.

For example, to factor to $2x^3 - 50x$ completely, begin by finding the GCF.

The GCF of the expression is $2x$: $2x(x^2 - 25)$.

Now, factor the difference of squares: $2x(x - 5)(x + 5)$.

Another example: Follow the steps to factor $-16t^2 + 32t + 48$ completely.

a. First, factor out the GCF. (Remember: When you factor out a negative number, all the signs on the resulting factor change.)

b. Now look for ways to factor further. (Notice the quadratic expression factors.)

©2015 Great Minds eureka-math.org
ALG I-M4-SE-B2-1.3.1-10.2015

Lesson 3: Advanced Factoring Strategies for Quadratic Expressions

Classwork

Opening Exercise

Carlos wants to build a sandbox for his little brother. He is deciding between a square sandbox with side lengths that can be represented by $x + 3$ units and a rectangular sandbox with a length 1 unit more than the side of the square and width 1 unit less than the side of the square.

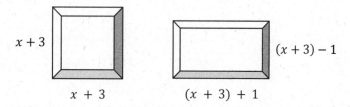

Carlos thinks the areas should be the same because one unit is just moved from one side to the other.

a. Do you agree that the two areas should be the same? Why or why not?

b. How would you write the expressions that represent the length and width of the rectangular sandbox in terms of the side length of the square?

c. If you use the expressions for length and width represented in terms of the side length of the square, can you then write the area of the rectangle in the same terms?

d.   How can this expression be seen as the product of a sum and difference: $(a + b)(a - b)$?

e.   Can you now rewrite the area expression for the rectangle as the difference of squares: $(a + b)(a - b) = a^2 - b^2$?

f.   Look carefully at your answer to the last question. What does it tell you about the areas of the two shapes?

g.   Can you verify that our algebra is correct using a diagram or visual display?

EUREKA
MATH™

©2015 Great Minds eureka-math.org
ALG I-M4-SE-B2-1.3.1-10.2015

Example 1

In Lesson 2, we saw that factoring is the reverse process of multiplication. We factor a polynomial by reversing the distribution process.

Consider the following example of multiplication:

$$(x + 3)(x + 5) \;\;\rightarrow\;\; x^2 + 5x + 3x + 15 \;\;\rightarrow\;\; x^2 + 8x + 15.$$

When we compare the numbers in the factored form with the numbers in the expanded form, we see that 15 is the product of the two numbers $(3 \cdot 5)$, and 8 is their sum $(3 + 5)$. The latter is even more obvious when we look at the expanded form before the like terms are combined.

Can you explain why that relationship exists between the numbers in the factors and the numbers in the final expanded form?

Example 2

Now compare the expansion of this binomial product to the one above:

$$(2x + 3)(1x + 5) \;\;\rightarrow\;\; 2x^2 + 10x + 3x + 15 \;\;\rightarrow\;\; 2x^2 + 13x + 15.$$

In the expression lying between the two arrows (before the like terms are combined), we can see the coefficients of the "split" linear terms $(+10x + 3x)$. Also notice that for this example, we have coefficients on both x-terms in the factors and that one of the coefficients is not 1. We have 2 and 1 as the factors of the leading coefficient in the expanded form and 3 and 5 as the factors of the constant term. Get ready for quadratic expressions in factored form where neither of the x-term coefficients are 1.

    a.   How is this product different from the first example? How is it similar?

    b.   Why are the "split" linear terms different in the two examples?

c. Now that we have four different numbers (coefficients) in each form of the expression, how can we use the numbers in the expanded form of the quadratic expression on the right to find the numbers in the factors on the left?

d. Now we need to place those numbers into the parentheses for the factors so that the product matches the expanded form of the quadratic expression. Here is a template for finding the factors using what we call the product-sum method:

$(\_\_x \pm \_\_)(\_\_x \pm \_\_)$ [We have four number places to fill in this factor template.]

$(\_\_x \pm 3)(\_\_x \pm 5)$ [We know that the 3 and 5 are the correct factors for 15, so we start there.]

$(2x \pm 3)(1x \pm 5)$ [We know that 2 and 1 are the only factors of 2, with the 2 opposite the 5 so that the distribution process gives us $10x$ for one product.]

$(2x + 3)(x + 5)$ [Finally, we know, at least for this example, that all the numbers are positive.]

Example 3

Now try factoring a quadratic expression with some negative coefficients: $3x^2 - x - 4$.

$(\_\_x \pm \_\_)(\_\_x \pm \_\_)$ [We have four number places to fill in this factor template.]

$(\_\_x \pm 1)(\_\_x \pm 4)$ [We know that ± 1 and ± 4 or ± 2 and ± 2 are the only possible factors for the constant term, -4, so we start there. Try 1 and 4 to start, and if that does not work, go back and try ± 2 and ± 2. We know that only one of the numbers can be negative to make the product negative.]

$(1x \pm 1)(3x \pm 4)$ [We know that 3 and 1 are the only factors of 3. We also know that both of these are positive (or both negative). But we do not know which positions they should take, so we will try both ways to see which will give a sum of -1.]

$(x + 1)(3x - 4)$ [Finally, we determine the two signs needed to make the final product $3x^2 - x - 4$.]

Exercises

For Exercises 1–6, factor the expanded form of these quadratic expressions. Pay particular attention to the negative and positive signs.

1. $3x^2 - 2x - 8$

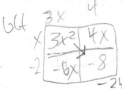

2. $3x^2 + 10x - 8$

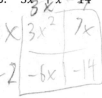

3. $3x^2 + x - 14$ [Notice that there is a 1 as a coefficient in this one.]

4. $2x^2 - 21x - 36$ [This might be a challenge. If it takes too long, try the next one.]

5. $-2x^2 + 3x + 9$ [This one has a negative on the leading coefficient.]

6. $r^2 + \frac{6}{4}r + \frac{9}{16}$ [We need to try one with fractions, too.]

For Exercises 7–10, use the structure of these expressions to factor completely.

7. $100x^2 - 20x - 63$

8. $y^4 + 2y^2 - 3$

9. $9x^2 - 3x - 12$

10. $16a^2b^4 + 20ab^2 - 6$

Lesson 3:   Advanced Factoring Strategies for Quadratic Expressions

©2015 Great Minds eureka-math.org
ALG I-M4-SE-B2-1.3.1-10.2015

EUREKA MATH™

Lesson 4: Advanced Factoring Strategies for Quadratic Expressions

Opening Exercise

Factor the following quadratic expressions.

    a. $2x^2 + 10x + 12$

    b. $6x^2 + 5x - 6$

Example: Splitting the Linear Term

How might we find the factors of $6x^2 + 5x - 6$?

1.   Consider the product $(a)(c)$: $(6)(-6) = -36$.

2.   Discuss the possibility that a and c are also multiplied when the leading coefficient is 1.

3.   List all possible factor pairs of $(a)(c)$: $(1, -36), (-1, 36), (2, -18), (-2, 18), (3, -12), (-3, 12), (4, -9), (-4, 9)$, and $(-6, 6)$.

4.   Find the pair that satisfies the requirements of the product-sum method (i.e., a pair of numbers whose product equals ac and whose sum is b): $(-4) + 9 = 5$.

5.   Rewrite the expression with the same first and last term but with an expanded b term using that pair of factors as coefficients: $6x^2 - 4x + 9x - 6$.

6.   We now have four terms that can be entered into a tabular model or factored by grouping.

7.   Factoring by grouping: Take the four terms above and pair the first two and the last two; this makes two *groups*.

    $[6x^2 - 4x] + [9x - 6]$ [Form two groups by pairing the first two and the last two.]

    $[2x(3x - 2)] + [3(3x - 2)]$ [Factor out the GCF from each pair.]

    The common binomial factor is now visible as a common factor of each group. Now rewrite by carefully factoring out the common factor, $3x - 2$, from each group: $(3x - 2)(2x + 3)$.

Note that we can factor difficult quadratic expressions, such as $6x^2 + 5x - 6$, using a tabular model or by splitting the linear term algebraically. Try both ways to see which one works best for you.

Exercise

Factor the following expressions using your method of choice. After factoring each expression completely, check your answers using the distributive property. Remember to always look for a GCF prior to trying any other strategies.

1. $2x^2 - x - 10$

2. $6x^2 + 7x - 20$

3. $-4x^2 + 4x - 1$

4. The area of a particular triangle can be represented by $x^2 + \frac{3}{2}x - \frac{9}{2}$. What are its base and height in terms of x?

©2015 Great Minds eureka-math.org
ALG I-M4-SE-B2-1.3.1-10.2015

Lesson Summary

While there are several steps involved in splitting the linear term, it is a relatively more efficient and reliable method for factoring trinomials in comparison to simple guess-and-check.

Problem Set

1. Factor completely.

    a. $9x^2 - 25x$

    b. $9x^2 - 25$

    c. $9x^2 - 30x + 25$

    d. $2x^2 + 7x + 6$

    e. $6x^2 + 7x + 2$

    f. $8x^2 + 20x + 8$

    g. $3x^2 + 10x + 7$

    h. $x^2 + \frac{11}{2}x + \frac{5}{2}$

    i. $6x^3 - 2x^2 - 4x$ [Hint: Look for a GCF first.]

2. The area of the rectangle below is represented by the expression $18x^2 + 12x + 2$ square units. Write two expressions to represent the dimensions, if the length is known to be twice the width.

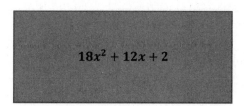

$$18x^2 + 12x + 2$$

3. Two mathematicians are neighbors. Each owns a separate rectangular plot of land that shares a boundary and has the same dimensions. They agree that each has an area of $2x^2 + 3x + 1$ square units. One mathematician sells his plot to the other. The other wants to put a fence around the perimeter of his new combined plot of land. How many linear units of fencing does he need? Write your answer as an expression in x.

   Note: This question has two correct approaches and two different correct solutions. Can you find them both?

EUREKA
MATH™

Lesson 4:   Advanced Factoring Strategies for Quadratic Expressions

S.25

©2015 Great Minds eureka-math.org
ALG I-M4-SE-B2-1.3.1-10.2015

This page intentionally left blank

Lesson 5: The Zero Product Property

Classwork

Opening Exercise

Consider the equation $a \cdot b \cdot c \cdot d = 0$. What values of a, b, c, and d would make the equation true?

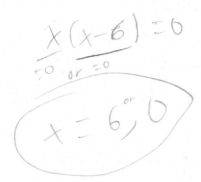
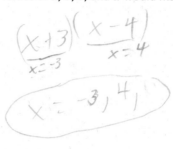

Exercises 1–4

Find values of c and d that satisfy each of the following equations. (There may be more than one correct answer.)

1. $cd = 0$

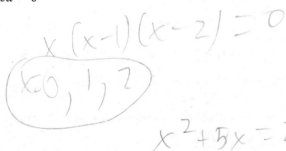

2. $(c - 5)d = 2$

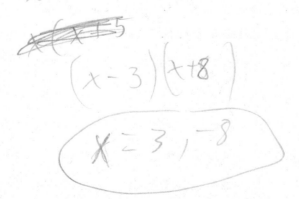

3. $(c - 5)d = 0$

4. $(c - 5)(d + 3) = 0$

Example 1

For each of the related questions below, use what you know about the zero product property to find the answers.

a. The area of a rectangle can be represented by the expression $x^2 + 2x - 3$. If the dimensions of the rectangle are known to be the linear factors of the expression, write each dimension of this rectangle as a binomial. Write the area in terms of the product of the two binomials.

b. Draw and label a diagram that represents the rectangle's area.

EUREKA
MATH™

c.   Suppose the rectangle's area is 21 square units. Can you find the dimensions of the rectangle?

d.   Rewrite the equation so that it is equal to zero and solve.

e.   What are the actual dimensions of the rectangle?

f.   A smaller rectangle can fit inside the first rectangle, and it has an area that can be represented by the expression $x^2 - 4x - 5$. If the dimensions of the rectangle are known to be the linear factors of the expression, what are the dimensions of the smaller rectangle in terms of x?

g.   What value for x would make the smaller rectangle have an area of $\frac{1}{3}$ that of the larger?

EUREKA
MATH™

Lesson 5:   The Zero Product Property

S.29

©2015 Great Minds eureka-math.org
ALG I-M4-SE-B2-1.3.1-10.2015

Exercises 5–8

Solve. Show your work.

5. $x^2 - 11x + 19 = -5$

$$+5 \quad +5$$

$$x^2 - 11x + 24 = 0$$

$$(x - 3)(x - 8) = 0$$

$$x = 3, 8$$

6. $7x^2 + x = 0$

$$x(7x + 1) = 0$$

$$x = 0, -\frac{1}{7}$$

7. $7r^2 - 14r = -7$

$$+7$$

$$7r^2 - 14r + 7 = 0$$

$$7(r^2 - 2r + 1)$$

$$7(r - 1)(r - 1)$$

8. $2d^2 + 5d - 12 = 0$

Lesson 5:   The Zero Product Property

EUREKA
MATH™

Lesson 6: Solving Basic One-Variable Quadratic Equations

Classwork

Example 1

A physics teacher put a ball at the top of a ramp and let it roll down toward the floor. The class determined that the height of the ball could be represented by the equation $h = -16t^2 + 4$, where the height, h, is measured in feet from the ground and time, t, is measured in seconds.

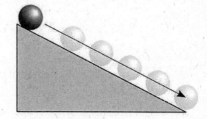

a.   What do you notice about the structure of the quadratic expression in this problem?

b.   In the equation, explain what the 4 represents.

c.   Explain how you would use the equation to determine the time it takes the ball to reach the floor.

d.   Now consider the two solutions for t. Which one is reasonable? Does the final answer make sense based on this context? Explain.

Example 2

Lord Byron is designing a set of square garden plots so some peasant families in his kingdom can grow vegetables. The minimum size for a plot recommended for vegetable gardening is at least 2 m on each side. Lord Byron has enough space around the castle to make bigger plots. He decides that each side should be the minimum (2 m) plus an additional x m.

 a. What expression can represent the area of one individual garden based on the undecided additional length x?

 b. There are 12 families in the kingdom who are interested in growing vegetables in the gardens. What equation can represent the total area, A, of the 12 gardens?

 c. If the total area available for the gardens is 300 sq m, what are the dimensions of each garden?

 d. Find both values for x that make the equation in part (c) true (the solution set). What value of x does Lord Byron need to add to the 2 m?

©2015 Great Minds eureka-math.org
ALG I-M4-SE-B2-1.3.1-10.2015

Exercises

Solve each equation. Some of them may have radicals in their solutions.

1. $3x^2 - 9 = 0$

2. $(x - 3)^2 = 1$

3. $4(x - 3)^2 = 1$

4. $2(x - 3)^2 = 12$

5. Analyze the solutions for Exercises 2–4. Notice how the questions all had $(x - 3)^2$ as a factor, but each solution was different (radical, mixed number, whole number). Explain how the structure of each expression affected each problem-solution pair.

6. Peter is a painter, and he wonders if he would have time to catch a paint bucket dropped from his ladder before it hits the ground. He drops a bucket from the top of his 9-foot ladder. The height, h, of the bucket during its fall can be represented by the equation, $h = -16t^2 + 9$, where the height is measured in feet from the ground, and the time since the bucket was dropped, t, is measured in seconds. After how many seconds does the bucket hit the ground? Do you think he could catch the bucket before it hits the ground?

EUREKA
MATH™

Lesson Summary

By looking at the structure of a quadratic equation (missing linear terms, perfect squares, factored expressions), you can find clues for the best method to solve it. Some strategies include setting the equation equal to zero, factoring out the GCF or common factors, and using the zero product property.

Be aware of the domain and range for a function presented in context, and consider whether answers make sense in that context.

Problem Set

1. Factor completely: $15x^2 - 40x - 15$.

Solve each equation.

2. $4x^2 = 9$

3. $3y^2 - 8 = 13$

4. $(d + 4)^2 = 5$

5. $4(g - 1)^2 + 6 = 13$

6. $12 = -2(5 - k)^2 + 20$

7. Mischief is a toy poodle that competes with her trainer in the agility course. Within the course, Mischief must leap through a hoop. Mischief's jump can be modeled by the equation $h = -16t^2 + 12t$, where h is the height of the leap in feet and t is the time since the leap, in seconds. At what values of t does Mischief start and end the jump?

This page intentionally left blank

Lesson 7: Creating and Solving Quadratic Equations in One Variable

Classwork

Opening Exercise

The length of a rectangle is 5 in. more than twice a number. The width is 4 in. less than the same number. The perimeter of the rectangle is 44 in. Sketch a diagram of this situation, and find the unknown number.

$$5 + 2x \quad 19 \qquad p = 44 \text{ in.}$$
$$\text{perimeter}$$

$$x - 4$$
$$3$$

$$5 + 2x + 5 + 2x + x - 4 + x - 4 = 44 \text{ in.}$$
$$\text{perimeter}$$

$$6x + 2 = 44$$
$$\quad -2 \quad -2$$

$$\frac{6x}{6} = \frac{42}{6} \qquad \boxed{x = 7}$$

Example 1

The length of a rectangle is 5 in. more than twice a number. The width is 4 in. less than the same number. If the area of the rectangle is 15 in^2, find the unknown number.

$$5 + 2(5)$$

$$A = 15 \text{ in}^2$$

$$(x - 4)(5 + 2x) = 15$$

$$5x + 2x^2 - 20 - 8x = 15$$

$$2x^2 - 3x - 20 = 15$$
$$\qquad\qquad -15 \quad -15$$

$$2x^2 - 3x - 35 = 0$$

$$(2x + 7)(x - 5)$$

$$15$$

$$= 1$$

so area is 15.

Example 2

A picture has a height that is $\frac{4}{3}$ its width. It is to be enlarged so that the ratio of height to width remains the same, but the area is 192 in². What are the dimensions of the enlargement?

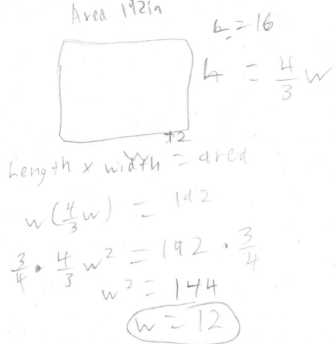

Area 192 in

$L = 16$

$L = \frac{4}{3} w$

Length × width = area

$w\left(\frac{4}{3}w\right) = 192$

$\frac{3}{4} \cdot \frac{4}{3} w^2 = 192 \cdot \frac{3}{4}$

$w^2 = 144$

$w = 12$

Exercises

Solve the following problems. Be sure to indicate if a solution is to be rejected based on the contextual situation.

1. The length of a rectangle is 4 cm more than 3 times its width. If the area of the rectangle is 15 cm², find the width.

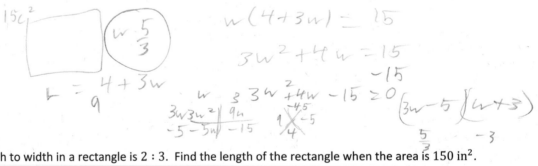

$15c^2$

$w \cdot \frac{5}{3}$

$w(4+3w) = 15$

$3w^2 + 4w = 15$

$L = 4 + 3w$

$3w^2 + 4w - 15 = 0$

$(3w-5)(w+3)$

$\frac{5}{3} \qquad -3$

2. The ratio of length to width in a rectangle is 2 : 3. Find the length of the rectangle when the area is 150 in².

EUREKA MATH™

3. One base of a trapezoid is 4 in. more than twice the length of the second base. The height of the trapezoid is 2 in. less than the second base. If the area of the trapezoid is 4 in², find the dimensions of the trapezoid.

(Note: The area of a trapezoid is $A = \frac{1}{2}(b_1 + b_2)h$.)

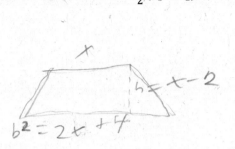

$$4 \text{ in}^2 = \frac{1}{2}(x + 2x + 4)(x - 2)$$

$$8 = (3x + 4)(x - 2)$$

$$8 = 3x^2 - 6x + 4x - 8$$

$$3x^2 - 2x - 8 = 8$$
$$\qquad\qquad -8 \quad -8$$
$$3x^2 - 2x - 16 = 0$$

$$(3x - 8)(x + 2)$$

$$\frac{8}{3}, -2$$

$$b = x - 2$$

$$b^2 = 2x + 4$$

4. A garden measuring 12 m by 16 m is to have a pedestrian pathway that is w meters wide installed all the way around it, increasing the total area to 285 m². What is the width, w, of the pathway?

5. Karen wants to plant a garden and surround it with decorative stones. She has enough stones to enclose a rectangular garden with a perimeter of 68 ft., and she wants the garden to cover 240 ft². What is the length and width of her garden?

6. Find two consecutive odd integers whose product is 99. (Note: There are two different pairs of consecutive odd integers and only an algebraic solution will be accepted.)

7. Challenge: You have a 500-foot roll of chain link fencing and a large field. You want to fence in a rectangular playground area. What are the dimensions of the largest such playground area you can enclose? What is the area of the playground?

EUREKA
MATH™

Lesson 8: Exploring the Symmetry in Graphs of Quadratic Functic

Classwork

Graph Vocabulary

coefficent *(handwritten)*
leading *(handwritten)*

AXIS OF SYMMETRY: Given a quadratic function in standard form, $f(x) = ax^2 + bx + c$, the vertical line given by the   h of the equation $x = -\dfrac{b}{2a}$ is called the *axis of symmetry* of the graph of the quadratic function.

VERTEX: The point where the graph of a quadratic function and its axis of symmetry intersect is called the *vertex*.

END BEHAVIOR OF A GRAPH: Given a quadratic function in the form $f(x) = ax^2 + bx + c$ (or $f(x) = a(x - h)^2 + k$), th quadratic function is said to *open up* if $a > 0$ and *open down* if $a < 0$.

- If $a > 0$, then f has a minimum at the x-coordinate of the vertex; that is, f is decreasing for x-values less t (or to the left of) the vertex, and f is increasing for x-values greater than (or to the right of) the vertex.

- If $a < 0$, then f has a maximum at the x-coordinate of the vertex; that is, f is increasing for x-values less th (or to the left of) the vertex, and f is decreasing for x-values greater than (or to the right of) the vertex.

infinite   or   (handwritten)

if a is + (handwritten)

if a is − (handwritten)

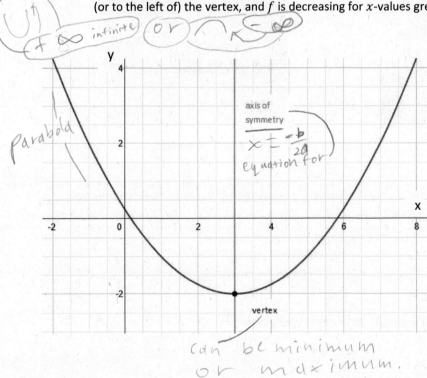

Parabola (handwritten)

axis of
symmetry

$x = \dfrac{-b}{2a}$

equation for (handwritten)

vertex

Can be minimum or maximum. (handwritten)

End behavior: This graph of a quadratic function opens up. As the values of x approach $+\infty$ and $-\infty$, the values of y approach $+\infty$.

Exploratory Challenge 1

Below are some examples of curves found in architecture around the world. Some of these might be represented by graphs of quadratic functions. What are the key features these curves have in common with a graph of a quadratic function?

St. Louis Arch

Bellos Falls Arch Bridge

Arch of Constantine

Roman Aqueduct

The photographs of architectural features above MIGHT be closely represented by graphs of quadratic functions. Answer the following questions based on the pictures.

    a.   How would you describe the overall shape of a graph of a quadratic function?

    b.   What is similar or different about the overall shape of the above curves?

IMPORTANT: Many of the photographs in this activity cannot actually be modeled with a quadratic function but rather are catenary curves. These are "quadratic-like" and can be used for our exploration purposes as they display many of the same features, including the symmetry we are exploring in this lesson.

EUREKA MATH

©2015 Great Minds eureka-math.org
ALG I-M4-SE-B2-1.3.1-10.2015

Exploratory Challenge 2

Use the graphs of quadratic functions (Graph A and Graph B) to fill in the table and answer the questions on the following page.

Graph A

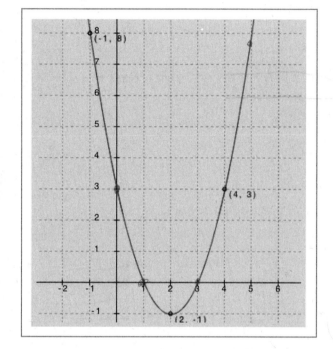

x	$f(x)$
−1	8
0	3
1	0
2	−1
3	0
4	3
5	8

Graph B

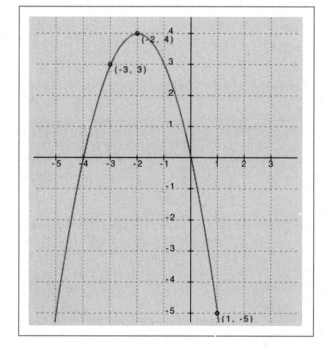

x	$f(x)$
−5	−5
−4	0
−3	3
−2	4
−1	3
0	0
1	−5

Use your graphs and tables of values from the previous page to fill in the blanks or answer the questions for each below.

		Graph A		Graph B	
1	x-Intercepts	1	3	4	0
2	Vertex	2, −1		−2, 4	
3	Sign of the Leading Coefficient	+		−	
4	Vertex Represents a Minimum or Maximum?	minimum		maximum	
5	Points of Symmetry	Find $f(-1)$ and $f(5)$. 8, 8 Is $f(7)$ greater than or less than 8? Explain greater curves up		Find $f(-1)$ and $f(-3)$. 3, 3 $f(2) = -12$. Predict the value for $f(-6)$ and explain your answer.	
6	Increasing and Decreasing Intervals	On what intervals of the domain is the function depicted by the graph increasing? On what intervals of the domain is the function depicted by the graph decreasing?		On what intervals of the domain is the function depicted by the graph increasing? On what intervals of the domain is the function depicted by the graph decreasing?	
7	Average Rate of Change on an Interval	What is the average rate of change for the following intervals? $[-1, 0]$: $[0, 1]$: $[0, 3]$: $[1, 3]$:		What is the average rate of change for the following intervals? $[-5, -4]$: $[-4, -3]$: $[-4, -1]$: $[-3, -1]$:	

Understanding the symmetry of quadratic functions and their graphs (Look at the tables and row 5 in the chart.)

a.   What patterns do you see in the tables of values you made next to Graph A and Graph B?

Finding the vertex and axis of symmetry (Look at rows 1 and 2 of the chart.)

b.   How can we know the x-coordinate of the vertex by looking at the x-coordinates of the zeros (or any pair of symmetric points)?

Understanding end behavior (Look at rows 3 and 4 of the chart.)

c.   What happens to the y-values of the functions as the x-values increase to very large numbers? What about as the x-values decrease to very small numbers (in the negative direction)?

d.   How can we know whether a graph of a quadratic function opens up or down?

©2015 Great Minds eureka-math.org
ALG I-M4-SE-B2-1.3.1-10.2015

Identifying intervals on which the function is increasing or decreasing (Look at row 6 in the chart.)

    e.   Is it possible to determine the exact intervals that a quadratic function is increasing or decreasing just by looking at a graph of the function?

Computing average rate of change on an interval (Look at row 7 in the chart.)

    f.   Explain why the average rate of change over the interval $[1, 3]$ for Graph A was zero.

    g.   How are finding the slope of a line and finding the average rate of change on an interval of a quadratic function similar? How are they different?

Finding a unique quadratic function:

    h.   Can you graph a quadratic function if you don't know the vertex? Can you graph a quadratic function if you only know the x-intercepts?

©2015 Great Minds eureka-math.org
ALG I-M4-SE-B2-1.3.1-10.2015

i.   Remember that we need to know at least two points to define a unique line. Can you identify a unique quadratic function with just two points? Explain.

j.   What is the minimum number of points needed to identify a unique quadratic function? Explain why.

Exploratory Challenge 3

Below you see only one side of the graph of a quadratic function. Complete the graph by plotting three additional points of the quadratic function. Explain how you found these points, and then fill in the table on the right.

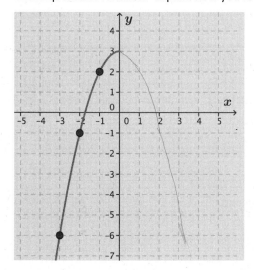

x	$f(x)$
-3	-6
-2	-1
-1	2
0	3
1	2
2	-1
3	-6

a.   What are the coordinates of the x-intercepts?

−1.8 , 1.8

b.   What are the coordinates of the y-intercept?

0,3

c.   What are the coordinates of the vertex? Is it a minimum or a maximum?

0,3   maximum

d.   If we knew the equation for this curve, what would the sign of the leading coefficient be?

e.   Verify that the average rate of change for the interval $-3 \le x \le -2$, or $[-3, -2]$, is 5. Show your steps.

f.   Based on your answer to row 6 in the table for Exploratory Challenge 2, what interval would have an average rate of change of -5? Explain.

Lesson 9: Graphing Quadratic Functions from Factored Form,

$$f(x) = a(x - m)(x - n)$$

Classwork

Opening Exercise

Solve the following equation.

$$x^2 + 6x - 40 = 0$$

Example 1

Consider the equation $y = x^2 + 6x - 40$.

    a.   Given this quadratic equation, can you find the point(s) where the graph crosses the x-axis?

    b.   In the last lesson, we learned about the symmetrical nature of the graph of a quadratic function. How can we use that information to find the vertex for the graph?

    c.   How could we find the y-intercept (where the graph crosses the y-axis and where $x = 0$)?

EUREKA
MATH™

Lesson 9:   Graphing Quadratic Functions from Factored Form,
$f(x) = a(x - m)(x - n)$

©2015 Great Minds eureka-math.org
ALG I-M4-SE-B2-1.3.1-10.2015

S.55

d. What else can we say about the graph based on our knowledge of the symmetrical nature of the graph of a quadratic function? Can we determine the coordinates of any other points?

e. Plot the points you know for this equation on graph paper, and connect them to show the graph of the equation.

Exercise 1

Graph the following functions, and identify key features of the graph.

a. $f(x) = -(x+2)(x-5)$

b. $g(x) = x^2 - 5x - 24$

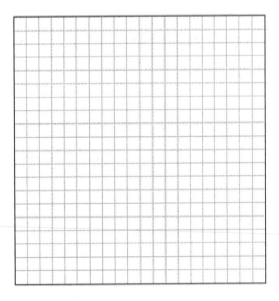

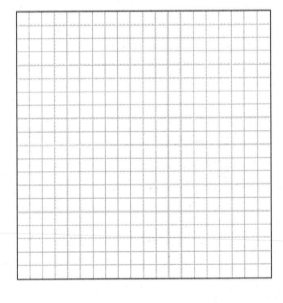

Lesson 9:   Graphing Quadratic Functions from Factored Form,
$f(x) = a(x-m)(x-n)$

EUREKA
MATH

c. $f(x) = 5(x - 2)(x - 3)$

d. $p(x) = -6x^2 + 42x - 60$

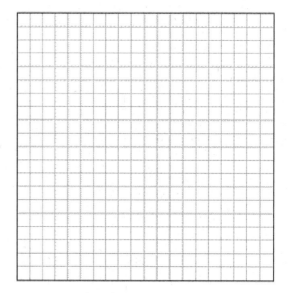

Example 2

Consider the graph of the quadratic function shown below with x-intercepts -4 and 2.

a.   Write a formula for a possible quadratic function, in factored form, that the graph represents using a as a constant factor.

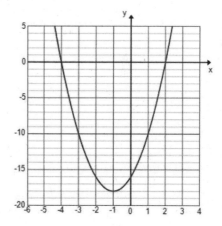

b.   The y-intercept of the graph is -16. Use the y-intercept to adjust your function by finding the constant factor a.

EUREKA MATH

Lesson 9:   Graphing Quadratic Functions from Factored Form,
$f(x) = a(x - m)(x - n)$

S.57

©2015 Great Minds eureka-math.org
ALG I-M4-SE-B2-1.3.1-10.2015

Exercise 2

Given the x-intercepts for the graph of a quadratic function, write a possible formula for the quadratic function, in factored form.

a. x-intercepts: 0 and 3

b. x-intercepts: -1 and 1

c. x-intercepts: -5 and 10

d. x-intercepts: $\frac{1}{2}$ and 4

Exercise 3

Consider the graph of the quadratic function shown below with x-intercept -2.

a. Write a formula for a possible quadratic function, in factored form, that the graph represents using a as a constant factor.

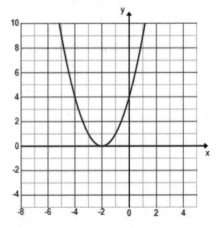

b. b. The y-intercept of the graph is 4. Use the y-intercept to adjust your function by finding the constant factor a.

Graphing Quadratic Functions from Factored Form,
$f(x) = a(x - m)(x - n)$

EUREKA
MATH™

Example 3

A science class designed a ball launcher and tested it by shooting a tennis ball straight up from the top of a 15-story building. They determined that the motion of the ball could be described by the function:

$$h(t) = -16t^2 + 144t + 160,$$

where t represents the time the ball is in the air in seconds and $h(t)$ represents the height, in feet, of the ball above the ground at time t. What is the maximum height of the ball? At what time will the ball hit the ground?

a.   With a graph, we can see the number of seconds it takes for the ball to reach its peak and how long it takes to hit the ground. How can factoring the expression help us graph this function?

b.   Once we have the function in its factored form, what do we need to know in order to graph it? Now graph the function.

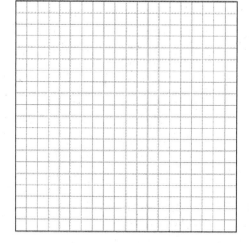

c.   Using the graph, at what time does the ball hit the ground?

d.   Over what domain is the ball rising? Over what domain is the ball falling?

e.   Using the graph, what is the maximum height the ball reaches?

EUREKA
MATH™

Lesson 9:   Graphing Quadratic Functions from Factored Form,
              $f(x) = a(x - m)(x - n)$

S.59

©2015 Great Minds eureka-math.org
ALG I-M4-SE-B2-1.3.1-10.2015

Exercise 4

The science class in Example 3 adjusted their ball launcher so that it could accommodate a heavier ball. They moved the launcher to the roof of a 23-story building and launched an 8.8-pound shot put straight up into the air. (Note: Olympic and high school women use the 8.8-pound shot put in track and field competitions.) The motion is described by the function $h(t) = -16t^2 + 32t + 240$, where $h(t)$ represents the height, in feet, of the shot put above the ground with respect to time t in seconds. (Important: No one was harmed during this experiment!)

    a.   Graph the function, and identify the key features of the graph.

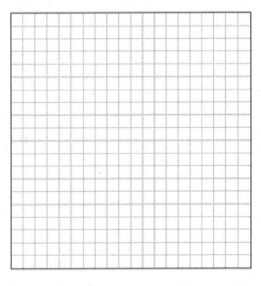

    b.   After how many seconds does the shot put hit the ground?

    c.   What is the maximum height of the shot put?

    d.   What is the value of $h(0)$, and what does it mean for this problem?

Lesson 9:   Graphing Quadratic Functions from Factored Form,
$f(x) = a(x - m)(x - n)$

©2015 Great Minds eureka-math.org
ALG I-M4-SE-B2-1.3.1-10.2015

EUREKA
MATH™

Lesson Summary

- When we have a quadratic function in factored form, we can find its x-intercepts, y-intercept, axis of symmetry, and vertex.

- For any quadratic equation, the roots are the solution(s) where $y = 0$, and these solutions correspond to the points where the graph of the equation crosses the x-axis.

- A quadratic equation can be written in the form $y = a(x - m)(x - n)$, where m and n are the roots of the function. Since the x-value of the vertex is the average of the x-values of the two roots, we can substitute that value back into the equation to find the y-value of the vertex. If we set $x = 0$, we can find the y-intercept.

Problem Set

1. Graph the following on your own graph paper, and identify the key features of the graph.

   a. $f(x) = (x - 2)(x + 7)$

   b. $h(x) = -3(x - 2)(x + 2)$

   c. $g(x) = -2(x - 2)(x + 7)$

   d. $h(x) = x^2 - 16$

   e. $p(x) = x^2 - 2x + 1$

   f. $q(x) = 4x^2 + 20x + 24$

2. A rocket is launched from a cliff. The relationship between the height of the rocket, h, in feet, and the time since its launch, t, in seconds, can be represented by the following function:
$$h(t) = -16t^2 + 80t + 384.$$

   a. Sketch the graph of the motion of the rocket.

   b. When does the rocket hit the ground?

   c. When does the rocket reach its maximum height?

   d. What is the maximum height the rocket reaches?

   e. At what height was the rocket launched?

3. Given the x-intercepts for the graph of a quadratic function, write a possible formula for the quadratic function, in factored form.

   a. x-intercepts: -1 and -6

   b. x-intercepts: -2 and $\frac{2}{3}$

   c. x-intercepts: -3 and 0

   d. x-intercept: 7

4. Suppose a quadratic function is such that its graph has x-intercepts of -3 and 2 and a y-intercept of 6.

   a. Write a formula for the quadratic function.

   b. Sketch the graph of the function.

EUREKA MATH™

Lesson 9:   Graphing Quadratic Functions from Factored Form,
$f(x) = a(x - m)(x - n)$

S.61

©2015 Great Minds eureka-math.org
ALG I-M4-SE-B2-1.3.1-10.2015

This page intentionally left blank

Lesson 10: Interpreting Quadratic Functions from Graphs and Tables

Classwork

Example 1

In a study of the activities of dolphins, a marine biologist made a 24-second video of a dolphin swimming and jumping in the ocean with a specially equipped camera that recorded one dolphin's position with respect to time. This graph represents a piecewise function, $y = f(t)$, that is defined by quadratic functions on each interval. It relates the dolphin's vertical distance from the surface of the water, in feet, to the time from the start of the video, in seconds. Use the graph to answer the questions below.

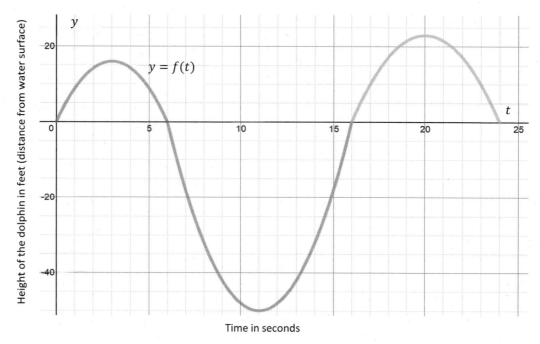

a.   Describe what you know for sure about the actions of the dolphin in the time interval from 0–6 sec. Can you determine the horizontal distance the dolphin traveled in that time interval? Explain why or why not.

b. Where do you find the values for which $f(t) = 0$? Explain what they mean in the context of this problem.

c. How long was the dolphin swimming under water in the recorded time period? Explain your answer or show your work.

d. Estimate the maximum height, in feet, that the dolphin jumped in the recorded 24-second time period? Explain how you determined your answer.

e. Locate the point on the graph where $f(t) = -50$, and explain what information the coordinates of that point give you in the context of this problem.

EUREKA
MATH™

Example 2

The table below represents the value of Andrew's stock portfolio, where V represents the value of the portfolio in hundreds of dollars and t is the time in months since he started investing. Answer the questions that follow based on the table of values.

t (months)	$V(t)$ (hundreds of dollars)
2	325
4	385
6	405
8	385
10	325
12	225
14	85
16	−95
18	−315

a. What kind of function could model the data in this table? How can you support your conclusion?

b. Assuming this data is in fact quadratic, how much did Andrew invest in his stock initially? Explain how you arrived at this answer.

EUREKA
MATH™

Lesson 10:   Interpreting Quadratic Functions from Graphs and Tables

©2015 Great Minds eureka-math.org
ALG I-M4-SE-B2-1.3.1-10.2015

S.65

A STORY OF FUNCTIONS

Lesson 10   M4

ALGEBRA I

c.   What is the maximum value of his stock, and how long did it take to reach the maximum value?

d.   If the pattern continues to follow the quadratic trend shown above, do you advise Andrew to sell or keep his stock portfolio? Explain why.

e.   How fast is Andrew's stock value decreasing between $[10, 12]$? Find another two-month interval where the average rate of change is faster than $[10, 12]$ and explain why.

f.   Are there other two-month intervals where the rate of change is the same as $[10, 12]$? Explain your answer.

EUREKA
MATH™

Lesson Summary

When interpreting quadratic functions and their graphs, it is important to note that the graph does not necessarily depict the path of an object. In the case of free-falling objects, for example, it is height with respect to time.

The y-intercept can represent the initial value of the function given the context, and the vertex represents the highest (if a maximum) or the lowest (if a minimum) value.

Problem Set

Pettitte and Ryu each threw a baseball into the air.

The vertical height of Pettitte's baseball is represented by the graph $y = P(t)$ below. P represents the vertical distance of the baseball from the ground in feet, and t represents time in seconds.

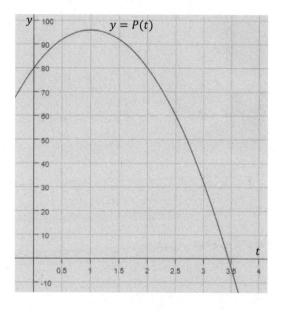

The vertical height of Ryu's baseball is represented by the table values $R(t)$ below. R represents the vertical distance of the baseball from the ground in feet, and t represents time in seconds.

t	$R(t)$
0	86
0.5	98
1	102
1.5	98
2	86
2.5	66
3	38
3.52	0

Use the functions on the previous page to answer the following questions.

a. Whose baseball reached the greatest height? Explain your answer.

b. Whose ball reached the ground fastest? Explain your answer.

c. Pettitte claims that his ball reached its maximum faster than Ryu's. Is his claim correct or incorrect? Explain your answer.

d. Find $P(0)$ and $R(0)$ values and explain what they mean in the problem. What conclusion can you make based on these values? Did Ryu and Pettitte throw their baseballs from the same height? Explain your answer.

e. Ryu claims that he can throw the ball higher than Pettitte. Is his claim correct or incorrect? Explain your answer.

EUREKA
MATH™

Lesson 11: Completing the Square

Classwork

Opening Exercise

Rewrite the following perfect square quadratic expressions in standard form. Describe patterns in the coefficients for the factored form, $(x + A)^2$, and the standard form, $x^2 + bx + c$.

FACTORED FORM	WRITE THE FACTORS	DISTRIBUTE	STANDARD FORM
Example: $(x + 1)^2$			
$(x + 2)^2$			
$(x + 3)^2$			
$(x + 4)^2$			
$(x + 5)^2$			
$(x + 20)^2$			

Example

Now try working backward. Rewrite the following standard form quadratic expressions as perfect squares.

STANDARD FORM	FACTORED FORM
$x^2 + 12x + 36$	
$x^2 - 12x + 36$	
$x^2 + 20x + 100$	
$x^2 - 3x + \dfrac{9}{4}$	
$x^2 + 100x + 2500$	
$x^2 + 8x + 3$	

Exploratory Challenge

Find an expression equivalent to $x^2 + 8x + 3$ that includes a perfect square binomial.

Exercises

Rewrite each expression by completing the square.

1. $a^2 - 4a + 15$

2. $n^2 - 2n - 15$

3. $c^2 + 20c - 40$

4. $x^2 - 1000x + 60\,000$

©2015 Great Minds eureka-math.org
ALG I-M4-SE-B2-1.3.1-10.2015

5. $y^2 - 3y + 10$

6. $k^2 + 7k + 6$

7. $z^2 - 0.2z + 1.5$

8. $p^2 + 0.5p + 0.1$

9. $j^2 - \frac{3}{4}j + \frac{3}{4}$

10. $x^2 - bx + c$

©2015 Great Minds eureka-math.org
ALG I-M4-SE-B2-1.3.1-10.2015

Lesson Summary

Just as factoring a quadratic expression can be useful for solving a quadratic equation, completing the square also provides a form that facilitates solving a quadratic equation.

Problem Set

Rewrite each expression by completing the square.

1. $q^2 + 12q + 32$

2. $m^2 - 4m - 5$

3. $x^2 - 7x + 6.5$

4. $a^2 + 70a + 1225$

5. $z^2 - 0.3z + 0.1$

6. $y^2 - 6by + 20$

7. Which of these expressions would be most easily rewritten by factoring? Justify your answer.

EUREKA
MATH™

Lesson 12: Completing the Square

Classwork

Opening Exercise

Rewrite each expression by completing the square.

   a. $z^2 - 5z + 8$

   b. $x^2 + 0.6x + 1$

Example 1

Now complete the square for $2x^2 + 16x + 3$.

Example 2

Business Application Vocabulary

UNIT PRICE (PRICE PER UNIT): The price per item a business sets to sell its product, which is sometimes represented as a linear expression.

QUANTITY: The number of items sold, sometimes represented as a linear expression.

REVENUE: The total income based on sales (but without considering the cost of doing business).

UNIT COST (COST PER UNIT) OR PRODUCTION COST: The cost of producing one item, sometimes represented as a linear expression.

PROFIT: The amount of money a business makes on the sale of its product. Profit is determined by taking the total revenue (the quantity sold multiplied by the price per unit) and subtracting the total cost to produce the items (the quantity sold multiplied by the production cost per unit): Profit = Total Revenue − Total Production Costs.

The following business formulas are used in this and the remaining lessons in the module:

Total Production Costs = (cost per unit)(quantity of items sold)

Total Revenue = (price per unit)(quantity of items sold)

Profit = Total Revenue − Total Production Costs

Now solve the following problem:

A certain business is marketing its product and has collected data on sales and prices for the past few years. The company determined that when it raised the selling price of the product, the number of sales went down. The cost of producing a single item is $10.

    a.   Using the data the company collected in this table, determine a linear expression to represent the quantity sold, q.

Selling Price (s)	Quantity Sold (q)
10	1,000
15	900
20	800
25	700

EUREKA
MATH™

b.   Now find an expression to represent the profit function, P.

Exercises

For Exercises 1–5, rewrite each expression by completing the square.

1. $3x^2 + 12x - 8$

2. $4p^2 - 12p + 13$

3. $\frac{1}{2}y^2 + 3y - 4$

4. $1.2n^2 - 3n + 6.5$

5. $\frac{1}{3}v^2 - 4v + 10$

6. A fast food restaurant has determined that its price function is $3 - \frac{x}{20\,000}$, where x represents the number of hamburgers sold.

    a. The cost of producing x hamburgers is determined by the expression $5000 + 0.56x$. Write an expression representing the profit for selling x hamburgers.

    b. Complete the square for your expression in part (a) to determine the number of hamburgers that need to be sold to maximize the profit, given this price function.

EUREKA
MATH™

Lesson Summary

Here is an example of completing the square of a quadratic expression of the form $ax^2 + bx + c$.

$$3x^2 - 18x - 2$$
$$3(x^2 - 6x) - 2$$
$$3(x^2 - 6x + 9) - 3(9) - 2$$
$$3(x - 3)^2 - 3(9) - 2$$
$$3(x - 3)^2 - 29$$

Problem Set

Rewrite each expression by completing the square.

1. $-2x^2 + 8x + 5$

2. $2.5k^2 - 7.5k + 1.25$

3. $\dfrac{4}{3}b^2 + 6b - 5$

4. $1000c^2 - 1250c + 695$

5. $8n^2 + 2n + 5$

EUREKA
MATH™

Lesson 12:   Completing the Square

S.77

©2015 Great Minds eureka-math.org
ALG I-M4-SE-B2-1.3.1-10.2015

This page intentionally left blank

Lesson 13: Solving Quadratic Equations by Completing the Square

Classwork

Opening Exercise

a. Solve the equation for b: $2b^2 - 9b = 3b^2 - 4b - 14$.

b. Rewrite the expression by completing the square: $\dfrac{1}{2}b^2 - 4b + 13$.

Example 1

Solve for x.

$$12 = x^2 + 6x$$

EUREKA MATH™

©2015 Great Minds eureka-math.org
ALG I-M4-SE-B2-1.3.1-10.2015

Rational and Irrational Numbers

The *sum or product of two rational numbers* is always a *rational number*.

The *sum of a rational number and an irrational number* is always an *irrational number*.

The *product of a rational number and an irrational number* is an *irrational number* as long as the rational number is not zero.

Example 2

Solve for x.

$$4x^2 - 40x + 94 = 0$$

Exercises

Solve each equation by completing the square.

1. $x^2 - 2x = 12$

Lesson 13:   Solving Quadratic Equations by Completing the Square

EUREKA MATH

2. $\frac{1}{2}r^2 - 6r = 2$

3. $2p^2 + 8p = 7$

4. $2y^2 + 3y - 5 = 4$

Lesson Summary

When a quadratic equation is not conducive to factoring, we can solve by completing the square.

Completing the square can be used to find solutions that are irrational, something very difficult to do by factoring.

Problem Set

Solve each equation by completing the square.

1. $p^2 - 3p = 8$

2. $2q^2 + 8q = 3$

3. $\frac{1}{3}m^2 + 2m + 8 = 5$

4. $-4x^2 = 24x + 11$

Lesson 14: Deriving the Quadratic Formula

Classwork

Opening Exercise

a.   Solve for x by completing the square: $x^2 + 2x = 8$.

b.   Solve for p by completing the square: $7p^2 - 12p + 4 = 0$.

Discussion

Solve $ax^2 + bx + c = 0$.

Exercises 1–4

Use the quadratic formula to solve each equation.

1. $x^2 - 2x = 12 \rightarrow a = 1, b = -2, c = -12$ [Watch the negatives.]

2. $\dfrac{1}{2}r^2 - 6r = 2 \rightarrow a = \dfrac{1}{2}, b = -6, c = -2$ [Did you remember the negative?]

3. $2p^2 + 8p = 7 \rightarrow a = 2, b = 8, c = -7$

4. $2y^2 + 3y - 5 = 4 \rightarrow a = 2, b = 3, c = -9$

©2015 Great Minds eureka-math.org
ALG I-M4-SE-B2-1.3.1-10.2015

Exercise 5

Solve these quadratic equations, using a different method for each: solve by factoring, solve by completing the square, and solve using the quadratic formula. Before starting, indicate which method you will use for each.

Method _____

$2x^2 + 5x - 3 = 0$

Method _____

$x^2 + 3x - 5 = 0$

Method _____

$\frac{1}{2}x^2 - x - 4 = 0$

Lesson Summary

The quadratic formula, $x = \dfrac{-b \pm \sqrt{b^2 - 4ac}}{2a}$, is derived by completing the square on the general form of a quadratic equation: $ax^2 + bx + c = 0$, where $a \neq 0$. The formula can be used to solve any quadratic equation, and is especially useful for those that are not easily solved using any other method (i.e., by factoring or completing the square).

Problem Set

Use the quadratic formula to solve each equation.

1. Solve for z: $z^2 - 3z - 8 = 0$.

2. Solve for q: $2q^2 - 8 = 3q$

3. Solve for m: $\dfrac{1}{3}m^2 + 2m + 8 = 5$.

EUREKA
MATH™

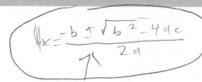

$$x = \frac{-b \pm \sqrt{b^2 - 4ac}}{2a}$$

Lesson 15: Using the Quadratic Formula

Classwork

Opening Exercise

Solve the following:

a. $4x^2 + 5x + 3 = 2x^2 - 3x$

$-2x^2 + 3x$

$2x^2 + 8x + 3 = 0$

$a = 2 \quad b = 8 \quad c = 3$

$x = \dfrac{-8 \pm \sqrt{8^2 - 4(2(3))}}{2(2)}$

$x = \dfrac{-8 \pm \sqrt{64 - 24}}{4}$

b. $c^2 - 14 = 5c$

$x^2 - 5x - 14 = 0$

$a = 1 \quad b = -5 \quad c = -14$

$x = \dfrac{5 \pm \sqrt{-5^2 - 4(1(-14))}}{2(1)}$

$\dfrac{5 \pm \sqrt{25 + 56}}{2}$

Exercises

Solve Exercises 1–5 using the quadratic formula.

1. $x^2 - 2x + 1 = 0$

$x^2 - 2x + 1 = 0$

$a = 1 \quad b = -2 \quad c = 1$

$x = \dfrac{2 \pm \sqrt{2^2 - 4}}{2}$

(1)

how many times a quadratic line crosses the x-axis is called the root, solution, or x-intercept.

discriminant tells how many solutions.

$b^2 - 4ac$

if $b^2 - 4ac > 0 = 2$ solutions

if $b^2 - 4ac = 0$ 1 solution

if $b^2 - 4ac < 0$ no real solutions.

$ax^2 + bx + c = 0$

$\div 2$

$\dfrac{-8 \pm \sqrt{40}}{}$

$x = \dfrac{-8 + 2\sqrt{10}}{4}$

$x = \dfrac{-4 \pm \sqrt{10}}{2}$

4 10

$\wedge \wedge \wedge$

2 2 2 5

crossing x at 2 spots

simplist form

$x = \dfrac{5 \pm \sqrt{89}}{2}$

$\dfrac{5 \pm 9}{2}$

7 or -2

points were it crosses x-axis.

2. $3b^2 + 4b + 8 = 0$

$3x^2 + 4x + 8 = 0$

$a = 3 \quad b = 4 \quad c = 8$

$x = \dfrac{-4 \pm \sqrt{4^2 - 4(3(8))}}{2(3)}$

$x = \dfrac{-4 \pm \sqrt{16 - 96}}{6}$

$x = \dfrac{-4 \pm \sqrt{-80}}{6}$

no solution

3. $2t^2 + 7t - 4 = 0$

$2x^2 + 7x - 4$

$a = 2 \quad b = 7 \quad c = -4$

$x = \dfrac{-7 \pm \sqrt{7^2 - 4(2(-4))}}{2(2)}$

$\dfrac{-7 \pm \sqrt{49 + 32}}{4}$

$\sqrt{81} \quad t = \dfrac{-7 \pm 9}{4}$

.5 or -4

$\dfrac{2}{4} = .5$

or

$-\dfrac{16}{4} = -4$

4. $q^2 - 2q - 1 = 0$

$q^2 - 2q - 1 = 0$

$a = 1 \quad b = 2 \quad c = -1$

$x = \dfrac{2 \pm \sqrt{2^2 - 4(1(-1))}}{2}$

$x = \dfrac{2 \pm \sqrt{8}}{2}$

$x = \dfrac{2 \pm 2\sqrt{2}}{2}$

$1 \pm \sqrt{2}$

5. $m^2 - 4 = 3$

EUREKA
MATH™

For Exercises 6–9, determine the number of real solutions for each quadratic equation without solving.

6. $p^2 + 7p + 33 = 8 - 3p$

7. $7x^2 + 2x + 5 = 0$

8. $2y^2 + 10y = y^2 + 4y - 3$

9. $4z^2 + 9 = -4z$

10. On the line below each graph, state whether the discriminant of each quadratic equation is positive, negative, or equal to zero. Then, identify which graph matches the discriminants below.

Graph 1	Graph 2	Graph 3	Graph 4
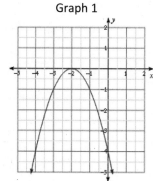	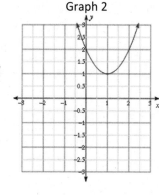	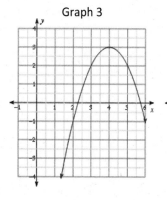	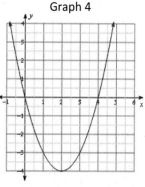

_____   _____   _____   _____

Discriminant A:
    $(-2)^2 - 4(1)(2)$

Graph: _____

Discriminant B:
    $(-4)^2 - 4(-1)(-4)$

Graph: _____

Discriminant C:
    $(-4)^2 - 4(1)(0)$

Graph: _____

Discriminant D:
    $(-8)^2 - 4(-1)(-13)$

Graph: _____

11. Consider the quadratic function $f(x) = x^2 - 2x - 4$.

    a.   Use the quadratic formula to find the x-intercepts of the graph of the function.

    b.   Use the x-intercepts to write the quadratic function in factored form.

    c.   Show that the function from part (b) written in factored form is equivalent to the original function.

Extension: Consider the quadratic equation $ax^2 + bx + c = 0$.

    a.   Write the equation in factored form, $a(x - m)(x - n) = 0$, where m and n are the solutions to the equation.

    b.   Show that the equation from part (a) is equivalent to the original equation.

©2015 Great Minds eureka-math.org
ALG I-M4-SE-B2-1.3.1-10.2015

Lesson 16: Graphing Quadratic Equations f m the Vertex Form, $y = a(x - h)^2 + k$

Classwork

Opening Exercise

Graph the equations $y = x^2$, $y = (x - 2)^2$, and $y = (x + 2)^2$ on the interval $-3 \leq 3$.

Exercises

1. Without graphing, state the vertex for each of the following quadratic equatio

    a. $y = (x - 5)^2 + 3$

    b. $y = x^2 - 2.5$

    c. $y = (x + 4)^2$

2. Write a quadratic equation whose graph will have the given vertex.

    a. $(1.9, -4)$

    b. $(0, 100)$

    c. $\left(-2, \dfrac{3}{2}\right)$

Exploratory Challenge

Caitlin has 60 feet of material that can be used to make a fence. Using this material, she wants to create a rectangular pen for her dogs to play in. What dimensions will maximize the area of the pen?

a. Let w be the width of the rectangular pen in feet. Write an expression that represents the length when the width is w feet.

b. Define a function that describes the area, A, in terms of the width, w.

c. Rewrite $A(w)$ in vertex form.

d. What are the coordinates of the vertex? Interpret the vertex in terms of the problem.

e. What dimensions maximize the area of the pen? Do you think this is a surprising answer?

S.94   Lesson 16:   Graphing Quadratic Equations from the Vertex Form,
$$y = a(x - h)^2 + k$$
©2015 Great Minds eureka-math.org
ALG I-M4-SE-B2-1.3.1-10.2015

EUREKA
MATH

> **Lesson Summary**
>
> When graphing a quadratic equation in vertex form, $y = a(x - h)^2 + k$, (h, k) are the coordinates of the vertex.

Problem Set

1. Find the vertex of the graphs of the following quadratic equations.

   a. $y = 2(x - 5)^2 + 3.5$

   b. $y = -(x + 1)^2 - 8$

2. Write a quadratic equation to represent a function with the following vertex. Use a leading coefficient other than 1.

   a. $(100, 200)$

   b. $\left(-\dfrac{3}{4}, -6\right)$

3. Use vocabulary from this lesson (i.e., *stretch, shrink, opens up,* and *opens down*) to compare and contrast the graphs of the quadratic equations $y = x^2 + 1$ and $y = -2x^2 + 1$.

This page intentionally left blank

Lesson 17: Graphing Quadratic Functions from the Standard Form, $f(x) = ax^2 + bx + c$

Classwork

Opening Exercise

A high school baseball player throws a ball straight up into the air for his math class. The math class was able to determine that the relationship between the height of the ball and the time since it was thrown could be modeled by the function $h(t) = -16t^2 + 96t + 6$, where t represents the time (in seconds) since the ball was thrown, and h represents the height (in feet) of the ball above the ground.

a. What does the domain of the function represent in this context?

b. What does the range of this function represent?

c. At what height does the ball get thrown?

d. After how many seconds does the ball hit the ground?

e. What is the maximum height that the ball reaches while in the air? How long will the ball take to reach its maximum height?

EUREKA MATH

Lesson 17:   Graphing Quadratic Functions from the Standard Form,
$f(x) = ax^2 + bx + c$

©2015 Great Minds eureka-math.org
ALG I-M4-SE-B2-1.3.1-10.2015

S.97

f.   What feature(s) of this quadratic function are *visible* since it is presented in the standard form, $f(x) = ax^2 + bx + c$?

g.   What feature(s) of this quadratic function are *visible* when it is rewritten in vertex form, $f(x) = a(x - h)^2 + k$?

A general strategy for graphing a quadratic function from the standard form:

Example

A high school baseball player throws a ball straight up into the air for his math class. The math class was able to determine that the relationship between the height of the ball and the time since it was thrown could be modeled by the function $h(t) = -16t^2 + 96t + 6$, where t represents the time (in seconds) since the ball was thrown, and h represents the height (in feet) of the ball above the ground.

a.   What do you notice about the equation, just as it is, that will help us in creating our graph?

b.   Can we factor to find the zeros of the function? If not, solve $h(t) = 0$ by completing the square.

S.98   Lesson 17:   Graphing Quadratic Functions from the Standard Form,
                                $f(x) = ax^2 + bx + c$

©2015 Great Minds eureka-math.org
ALG I-M4-SE-B2-1.3.1-10.2015

EUREKA
MATH

c.   What is the vertex of the function? What method did you use to find the vertex?

d.   Now plot the graph of $h(t) = -16t^2 + 96t + 6$ and label the key features on the graph.

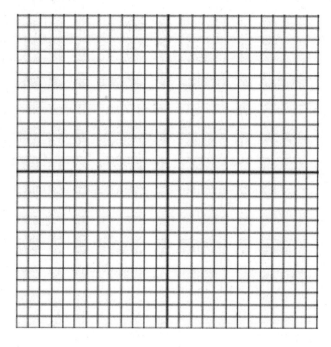

EUREKA
MATH™

Lesson 17:   Graphing Quadratic Functions from the Standard Form,
$f(x) = ax^2 + bx + c$

S.99

©2015 Great Minds eureka-math.org
ALG I-M4-SE-B2-1.3.1-10.2015

Exercises

1. Graph the function $n(x) = x^2 - 6x + 5$, and identify the key features.

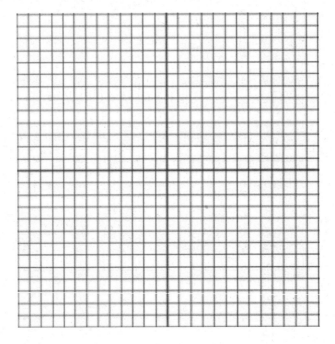

2. Graph the function $f(x) = \frac{1}{2}x^2 + 5x + 6$, and identify the key features.

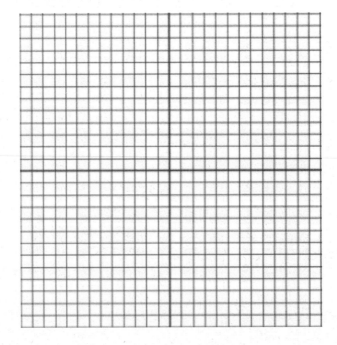

Lesson 17:   Graphing Quadratic Functions from the Standard Form,
$f(x) = ax^2 + bx + c$

EUREKA
MATH™

3. Paige wants to start a summer lawn-mowing business. She comes up with the following profit function that relates the total profit to the rate she charges for a lawn-mowing job:

$$P(x) = -x^2 + 40x - 100.$$

Both profit and her rate are measured in dollars. Graph the function in order to answer the following questions.

a. Graph P.

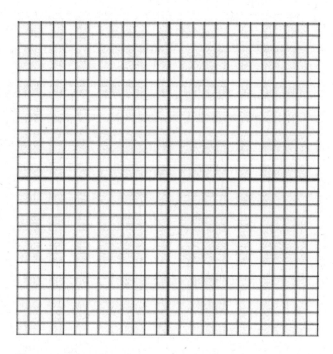

b. According to the function, what is her initial cost (e.g., maintaining the mower, buying gas, advertising)? Explain your answer in the context of this problem.

c. Between what two prices does she have to charge to make a profit?

d. If she wants to make $275 profit this summer, is this the right business choice?

EUREKA
MATH™

Lesson 17:   Graphing Quadratic Functions from the Standard Form,
              $f(x) = ax^2 + bx + c$

S.101

©2015 Great Minds eureka-math.org
ALG I-M4-SE-B2-1.3.1-10.2015

4. A student throws a bag of chips to her friend. Unfortunately, her friend does not catch the chips, and the bag hits the ground. The distance from the ground (height) for the bag of chips is modeled by the function $h(t) = -16t^2 + 32t + 4$, where h is the height (distance from the ground in feet) of the chips, and t is the number of seconds the chips are in the air.

   a. Graph h.

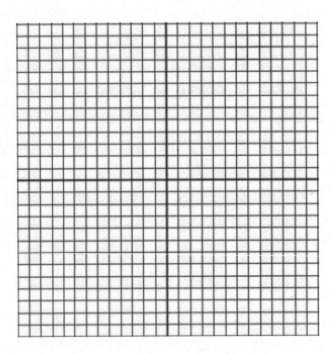

   b. From what height are the chips being thrown? Tell how you know.

   c. What is the maximum height the bag of chips reaches while airborne? Tell how you know.

   d. How many seconds after the bag was thrown did it hit the ground?

Lesson 17:   Graphing Quadratic Functions from the Standard Form,
                                $f(x) = ax^2 + bx + c$

                ©2015 Great Minds eureka-math.org
                ALG I-M4-SE-B2-1.3.1-10.2015

e. What is the average rate of change of height for the interval from 0 to $\frac{1}{2}$ second? What does that number represent in terms of the context?

f. Based on your answer to part (e), what is the average rate of change for the interval from 1.5 to 2 sec.?

5. Notice how the profit and height functions both have negative leading coefficients. Explain why this is.

EUREKA MATH

Lesson 17:   Graphing Quadratic Functions from the Standard Form,
$f(x) = ax^2 + bx + c$

S.103

©2015 Great Minds eureka-math.org
ALG I-M4-SE-B2-1.3.1-10.2015

Lesson Summary

The standard form of a quadratic function is $f(x) = ax^2 + bx + c$, where $a \neq 0$. A general strategy to graphing a quadratic function from the standard form:

- Look for hints in the function's equation for general shape, direction, and y-intercept.
- Solve $f(x) = 0$ to find the x-intercepts by factoring, completing the square, or using the quadratic formula.
- Find the vertex by completing the square or using symmetry. Find the axis of symmetry and the x-coordinate of the vertex using $\dfrac{-b}{2a}$ and the y-coordinate of the vertex by finding $f\left(\dfrac{-b}{2a}\right)$.
- Plot the points that you know (at least three are required for a unique quadratic function), sketch the graph of the curve that connects them, and identify the key features of the graph.

Problem Set

1. Graph $f(x) = x^2 - 2x - 15$, and identify its key features.

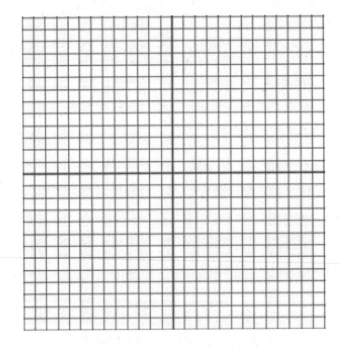

Lesson 17:   Graphing Quadratic Functions from the Standard Form,
$f(x) = ax^2 + bx + c$

EUREKA MATH

2. Graph $f(x) = -x^2 + 2x + 15$, and identify its key features.

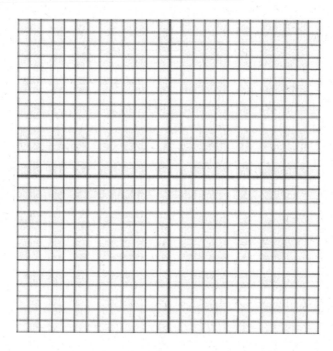

3. Did you recognize the numbers in the first two problems? The equation in the second problem is the product of -1 and the first equation. What effect did multiplying the equation by -1 have on the graph?

4. Giselle wants to run a tutoring program over the summer. She comes up with the following profit function:

$$P(x) = -2x^2 + 100x - 25$$

where x represents the price of the program. Between what two prices should she charge to make a profit? How much should she charge her students if she wants to make the most profit?

5. Doug wants to start a physical therapy practice. His financial advisor comes up with the following profit function for his business:

$$P(x) = -\frac{1}{2}x^2 + 150x - 10000$$

where x represents the amount, in dollars, that he charges his clients. How much will it cost for him to start the business? What should he charge his clients to make the most profit?

This page intentionally left blank

Lesson 18: Graphing Cubic, Square Root, and Cube Root Functions

Classwork

Opening Exercise

a.   Evaluate x^2 when $x = 7$.

b.   Evaluate $\sqrt{x}$ when $x = 81$.

c.   Evaluate x^3 when $x = 5$.

d.   Evaluate $\sqrt[3]{x}$ when $x = 27$.

Exploratory Challenge 1

Use your graphing calculator to create a data table for the functions $y = x^2$ and $y = \sqrt{x}$ for a variety of x-values. Use both negative and positive numbers, and round decimal answers to the nearest hundredth.

x	$y = x^2$	$y = \sqrt{x}$

EUREKA
MATH™

Lesson 18:   Graphing Cubic, Square Root, and Cube Root Functions

S.107

©2015 Great Minds eureka-math.org
ALG I-M4-SE-B2-1.3.1-10.2015

Exploratory Challenge 2

Create the graphs of $y = x^2$ and $y = \sqrt{x}$ on the same set of axes.

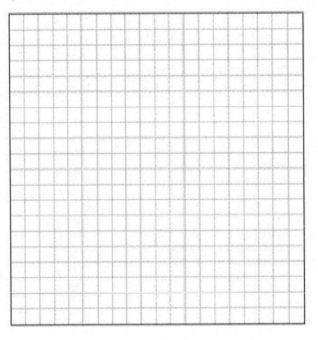

Exploratory Challenge 3

Create a data table for $y = x^3$ and $y = \sqrt[3]{x}$, and graph both functions on the same set of axes. Round decimal answers to the nearest hundredth.

x	$y = x^3$	$y = \sqrt[3]{x}$
-8		
-2		
-1		
0		
1		
2		
8		

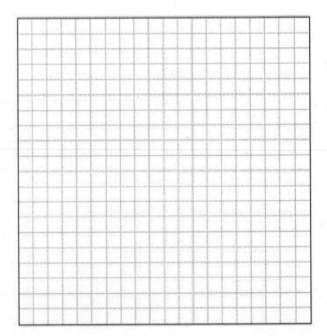

EUREKA
MATH™

Lesson Summary

- The square root parent function is a reflection of the quadratic parent function across the line $y = x$, when x is non-negative.

- The domain of quadratic, cubic, and cube root parent functions is all real numbers. The domain of the square root parent function is $x \geq 0$.

- The range of quadratic and square root parent functions is $[0, \infty)$. The range of the cubic and cube root parent functions is all real numbers.

- The cube root and cubic parent functions are symmetrical about the origin and are reflections of each other across the line $y = x$; the two operations reverse each other.

Problem Set

1. Create the graphs of the functions $f(x) = x^2 + 2$ and $g(x) = \sqrt{x} + 2$ using the given values. Use a calculator to help with decimal approximations.

x	$f(x)$	$g(x)$
-4		
-2		
-1		
0		
1		
2		
4		

2. What can be said about the first three values for $g(x)$ in the table?

3. Describe the relationship between the graphs given by the equations $y = x^2 + 2$ and $y = \sqrt{x} + 2$. How are they alike? How are they different?

4. Refer to your class notes for the graphs of $y = x^2$ and $y = \sqrt{x}$. How are the graphs of $y = x^2$ and $y = \sqrt{x}$ transformed to generate the graphs of $y = x^2 + 2$ and $y = \sqrt{x} + 2$?

EUREKA
MATH™

Lesson 18:   Graphing Cubic, Square Root, and Cube Root Functions

S.109

©2015 Great Minds eureka-math.org
ALG I-M4-SE-B2-1.3.1-10.2015

5. Create the graphs of $p(x) = x^3 - 2$ and $q(x) = \sqrt[3]{x} - 2$ using the given values for x. Use a calculator to help with decimal approximations.

x	$p(x)$	$q(x)$
-8		
-2		
-1		
0		
1		
2		
8		

6. For the table in Problem 5, explain why there were no function values that resulted in an error.

7. Describe the relationship between the domains and ranges of the functions $p(x) = x^3 - 2$ and $q(x) = \sqrt[3]{x} - 2$. Describe the relationship between their graphs.

8. Refer to your class notes for the graphs of $y = x^3$ and $y = \sqrt[3]{x}$. How are the graphs of $y = x^3$ and $y = \sqrt[3]{x}$ transformed to generate the graphs of $y = x^3 - 2$ and $y = \sqrt[3]{x} - 2$?

9. Using your responses to Problems 4 and 8, how do the functions given in Problems 1 and 5 differ from their parent functions? What effect does that difference seem to have on the graphs of those functions?

10. Create your own functions using $r(x) = x^2 - \boxed{}$ and $s(x) = \sqrt{x} - \boxed{}$ by filling in the box with a positive or negative number. Predict how the graphs of your functions will compare to the graphs of their parent functions based on the number that you put in the blank boxes. Generate a table of solutions for your functions, and graph the solutions.

Lesson 19: Translating Graphs of Functions

Classwork

Opening Exercise

Graph each set of three functions in the same coordinate plane (on your graphing calculator or a piece of graph paper). Then, explain what similarities and differences you see among the graphs.

a. $f(x) = x$
    $g(x) = x + 5$
    $h(x) = x - 6$

b. $f(x) = x^2$
    $g(x) = x^2 + 3$
    $h(x) = x^2 - 7$

c. $f(x) = |x|$
    $g(x) = |x + 3|$
    $h(x) = |x - 4|$

Example

For each graph, answer the following:

- What is the parent function?
- How does the translated graph relate to the graph of the parent function?
- Write the formula for the function depicted by the translated graph.

a.

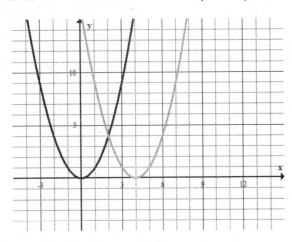

b.

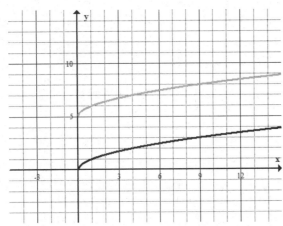

c.

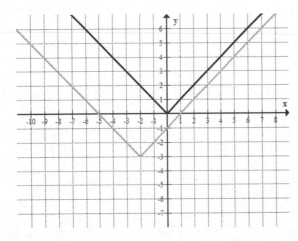

EUREKA
MATH™

Exercises

1. For each of the following graphs, use the formula for the parent function f to write the formula of the translated function.

a.

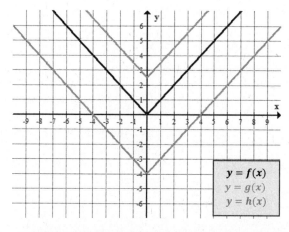

$y = f(x)$
$y = g(x)$
$y = h(x)$

b.

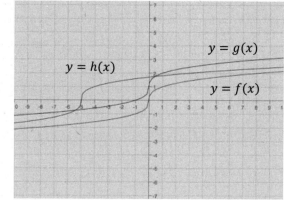

$y = g(x)$
$y = h(x)$
$y = f(x)$

2. Below is a graph of a piecewise function f whose domain is $-5 \le x \le 3$. Sketch the graphs of the given functions on the same coordinate plane. Label your graphs correctly.

$$g(x) = f(x) + 3 \qquad h(x) = f(x - 4)$$

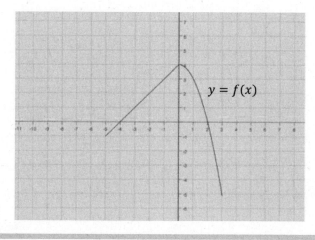

$y = f(x)$

3. Match the correct equation and description of the function with the given graphs.

Graphs	Equation	Description
$y = f(x)$ 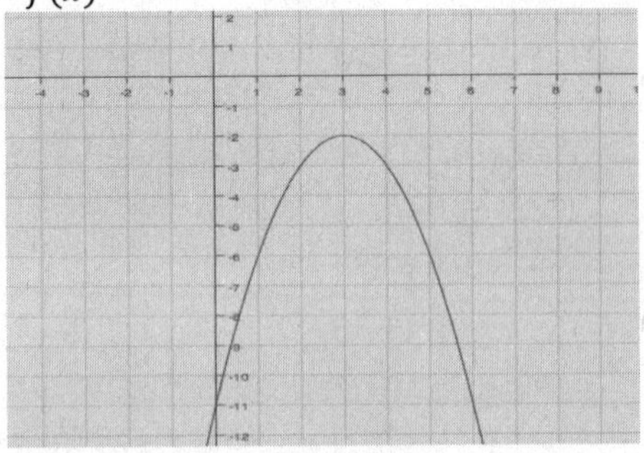 Equation _____ Description _____	E1. $y = (x - 3)^2$ E2. $y = (x + 2)^2 - 3$ E3. $y = -(x - 3)^2 - 2$ E4. $y = (x - 2)^2 - 3$	D1. The graph of the parent function is translated down 3 units and left 2 units. D2. The graph of the function does not have an x-intercept. D3. The coordinate of the y-intercept is $(0, 1)$, and both x-intercepts are positive. D4. The graph of the function has only one x-intercept.
$y = g(x)$ 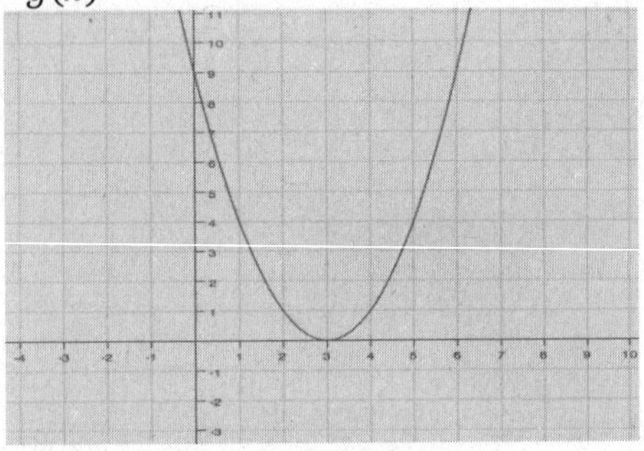 Equation _____ Description _____		
$y = h(x)$ 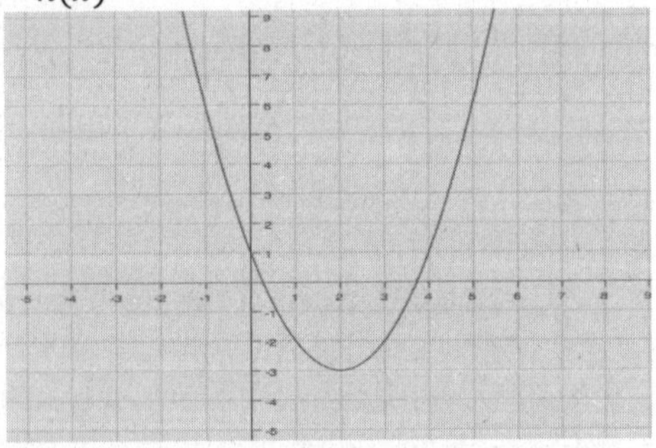 Equation _____ Description _____		
$y = p(x)$ 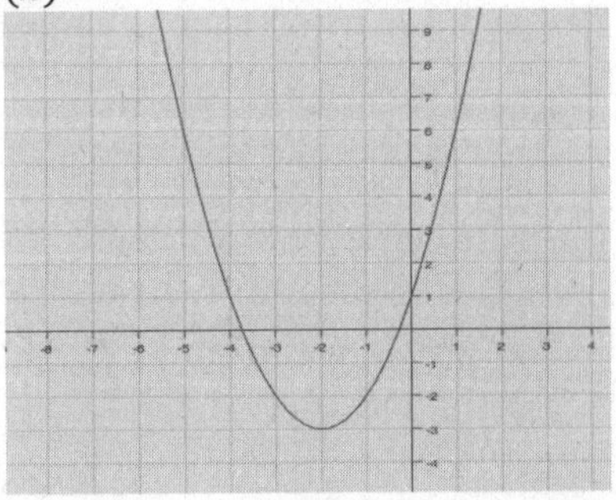 Equation _____ Description _____		

EUREKA
MATH™

Problem Set

1. Graph the functions in the same coordinate plane. Do not use a graphing calculator.

$$f(x) = \sqrt{x}$$
$$p(x) = 10 + \sqrt{x}$$
$$q(x) = \sqrt{x + 8}$$

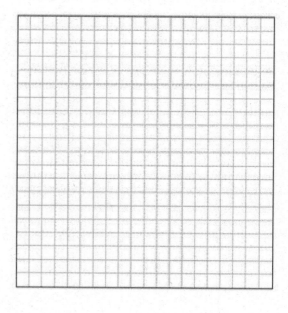

2. Write a function that translates the graph of the parent function $f(x) = x^2$ down 7.5 units and right 2.5 units.

3. How would the graph of $f(x) = |x|$ be affected if the function were transformed to $f(x) = |x + 6| + 10$?

4. Below is a graph of a piecewise function f whose domain is the interval $-4 \leq x \leq 2$. Sketch the graph of the given functions below. Label your graphs correctly.

$$g(x) = f(x) - 1 \qquad h(x) = g(x - 2) \text{ [Be careful; this one might be a challenge.]}$$

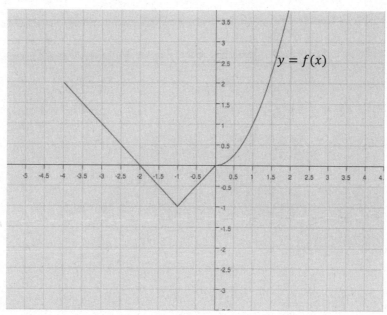

5. Study the graphs below. Identify the parent function and the transformations of that function depicted by the second graph. Then, write the formula for the transformed function.

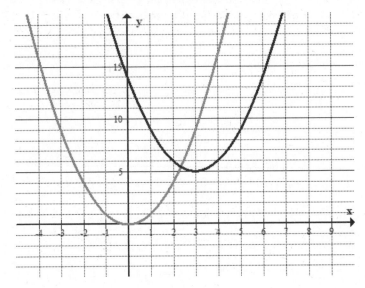

Lesson 19:   Translating Graphs of Functions

EUREKA
MATH™

Lesson 20: Stretching and Shrinking Graphs of Functions

Classwork

Opening Exercise

The graph of a quadratic function defined by $f(x) = x^2$ has been translated 5 units to the left and 3 units up. What is the formula for the function, g, depicted by the translated graph?

Sketch the graph of the equation $y = g(x)$.

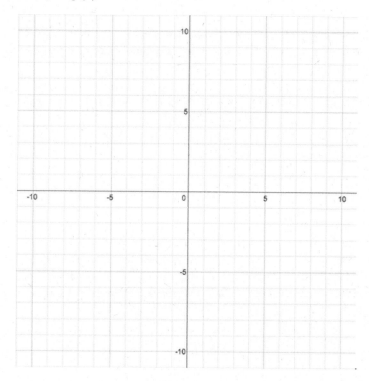

Example

Exploratory Challenge

Complete the following to review Module 3 concepts:

a. Consider the function $f(x) = |x|$. Complete the table of values for $f(x)$. Then, graph the equation $y = f(x)$ on the coordinate plane provided for part (b).

x	$f(x)$
-4	
-2	
0	
2	
4	

b. Complete the following table of values for each transformation of the function f. Then, graph the equations $y = g(x)$, $y = h(x)$, $y = j(x)$, and $y = k(x)$ on the same coordinate plane as the graph of $y = f(x)$. Label each graph.

x	$f(x)$	$g(x) = 3f(x)$	$h(x) = 2f(x)$	$j(x) = 0.5f(x)$	$k(x) = -2f(x)$
-4					
-2					
0					
2					
4					

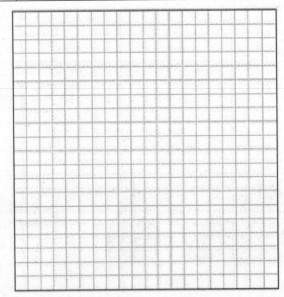

Lesson 20:   Stretching and Shrinking Graphs of Functions

EUREKA MATH

c. Describe how the graph of $y = kf(x)$ relates to the graph of $y = f(x)$ for each case.

   i. $k > 1$

   ii. $0 < k < 1$

   iii. $k = -1$

   iv. $-1 < k < 0$

   v. $k < -1$

d. Describe the transformation of the graph of f that results in the graphs of g, h, and k given the following formulas for each function. Then, graph each function and label each graph.

$f(x) = x^3$

$g(x) = 2x^3$

$h(x) = 0.5x^3$

$k(x) = -3x^3$

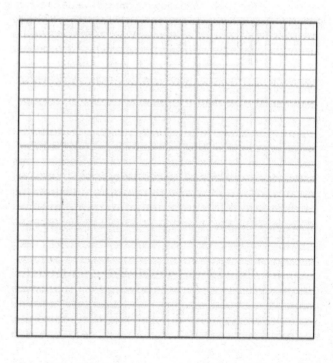

EUREKA
MATH™

©2015 Great Minds eureka-math.org
ALG I-M4-SE-B2-1.3.1-10.2015

e. Consider the function $f(x) = \sqrt[3]{x}$. Complete the table of values; then graph the equation $y = f(x)$.

x	$f(x)$
-8	
-1	
0	
1	
8	

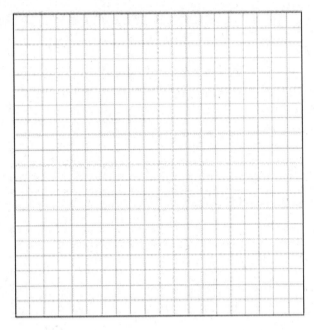

f. Complete the following table of values, rounding each value to the nearest hundredth. Graph the equations $y = g(x)$, $y = h(x)$, and $y = j(x)$ on the same coordinate plane as your graph of $y = f(x)$ above. Label each graph.

x	$f(x)$	$g(x) = f(2x)$	$h(x) = f(0.5x)$	$j(x) = f(-2x)$
-8				
-1				
0				
1				
8				

g. Describe the transformations of the graph of f that result in the graphs of g, h, and j.

EUREKA
MATH™

h.   Describe how the graph of $y = f\left(\frac{1}{k}x\right)$ relates to the graph of $y = f(x)$ for each case.

   i. $k > 1$

   ii. $0 < k < 1$

   iii. $k = -1$

   iv. $-1 < k < 0$

   v. $k < -1$

Exercise 1

For each of the sets below, answer the following questions:

   ▪   What are the parent functions?
   ▪   How does the transformed graph relate to the graph of the parent function?
   ▪   Write the formula for the function depicted by the transformed graph.

a.

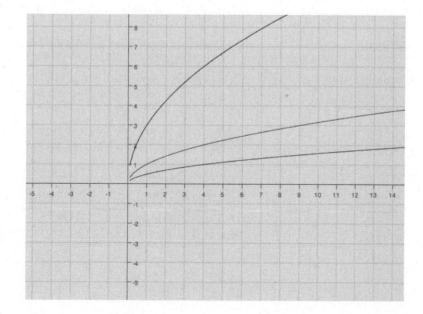

b.

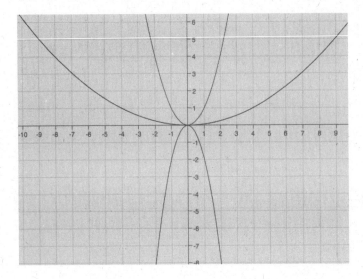

Exercise 2

Graph each set of functions in the same coordinate plane. Do not use a graphing calculator.

a. $f(x) = |x|$
    $g(x) = 4|x|$
    $h(x) = |2x|$
    $k(x) = -2|2x|$

b. $g(x) = \sqrt[3]{x}$
    $p(x) = 2\sqrt[3]{x}$
    $q(x) = -2\sqrt[3]{2x}$

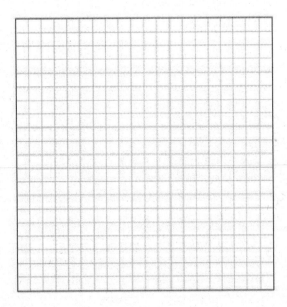

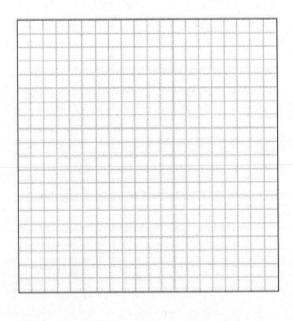

EUREKA
MATH™

Problem Set

1. Graph the functions in the same coordinate plane. Do not use a graphing calculator.

   $f(x) = |x|$

   $g(x) = 2|x|$

   $h(x) = |3x|$

   $k(x) = -3|3x|$

2. Explain how the graphs of functions $j(x) = 3|x|$ and $h(x) = |3x|$ are related.

3. Explain how the graphs of functions $q(x) = -3|x|$ and $r(x) = |-3x|$ are related.

4. Write a function, g, in terms of another function, f, such that the graph of g is a vertical shrink of the graph f by a factor of 0.75.

5. A teacher wants the students to write a function based on the parent function $f(x) = \sqrt[3]{x}$. The graph of f is stretched vertically by a factor of 4 and shrunk horizontally by a factor of $\frac{1}{3}$. Mike wrote $g(x) = 4\sqrt[3]{3x}$ as the new function, while Lucy wrote $h(x) = 3\sqrt[3]{4x}$. Which one is correct? Justify your answer.

6. Study the graphs of two different functions below. Which is a parent function? What is the constant value(s) multiplied to the parent function to arrive at the transformed graph? Now write the function defined by the transformed graph.

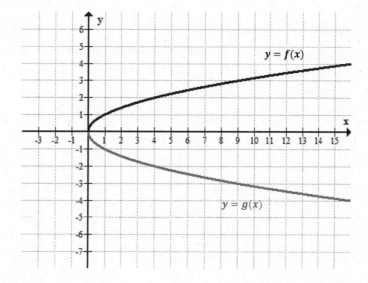

This page intentionally left blank

Lesson 21: Transformations of the Quadratic Parent Function, $f(x) = x^2$

Classwork

Example 1: Quadratic Expression Representing a Function

a. A quadratic function is defined by $g(x) = 2x^2 + 12x + 1$. Write this in the completed-square (vertex) form and show all the steps.

b. Where is the vertex of the graph of this function located?

c. Look at the completed-square form of the function. Can you name the parent function? How do you know?

d. What transformations have been applied to the parent function to arrive at function g? Be specific.

e. How does the completed-square form relate to the quadratic parent function $f(x) = x^2$?

Example 2

The graph of a quadratic function $f(x) = x^2$ has been translated 3 units to the right, vertically stretched by a factor of 4, and moved 2 units up. Write the formula for the function that defines the transformed graph.

Exercises

1. Without using a graphing calculator, sketch the graph of the following quadratic functions on the same coordinate plane, using transformations of the graph of the parent function $f(x) = x^2$.

    a. $g(x) = -2(x - 3)^2 + 4$

    b. $h(x) = -3(x + 5)^2 + 1$

    c. $k(x) = 2(x + 4)^2 - 3$

    d. $p(x) = x^2 - 2x$

    e. $t(x) = x^2 - 2x + 3$

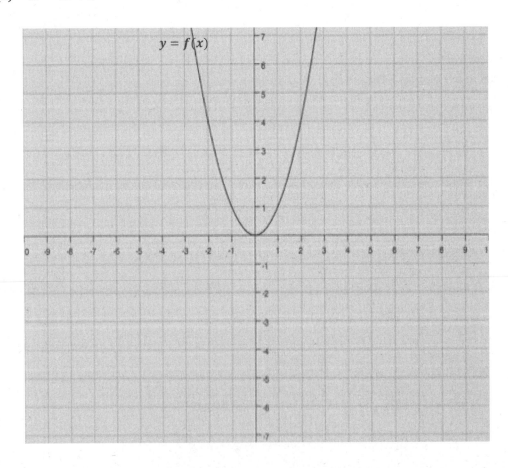

Lesson 21:   Transformations of the Quadratic Parent Function, $f(x) = x^2$

EUREKA
MATH

2. Write a formula for the function that defines the described transformation of the graph of the quadratic parent function $f(x) = x^2$.

    a. 3 units shift to the right

    b. Vertical shrink by a factor of 0.5

    c. Reflection across the x-axis

    d. 4 units shift up

    Then, graph both the parent and the transformed functions on the same coordinate plane.

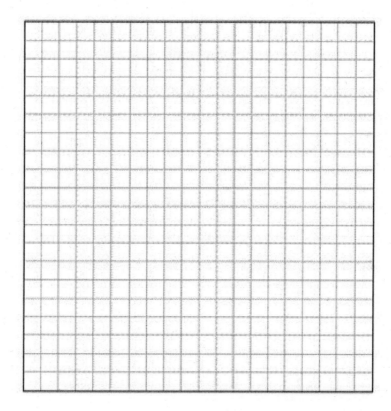

3. Describe the transformation of the quadratic parent function $f(x) = x^2$ that results in the quadratic function $g(x) = 2x^2 + 4x + 1$.

4. Sketch the graphs of the following functions based on the graph of the function $f(x) = x^2$. If necessary, rewrite some of the functions in the vertex (completed-square) form. Label your graphs.

    a. $g(x) = -(x - 4)^2 + 3$
    b. $h(x) = 3(x - 2)^2 - 1$
    c. $k(x) = 2x^2 + 8x$
    d. $p(x) = x^2 + 6x + 5$

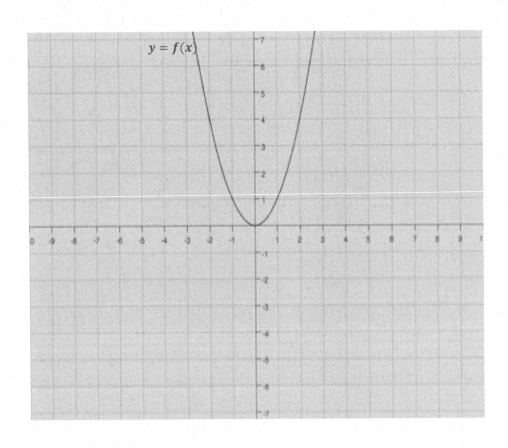

Lesson 21:   Transformations of the Quadratic Parent Function, $f(x) = x^2$

EUREKA
MATH™

Lesson Summary

Transformations of the quadratic parent function, $f(x) = x^2$, can be rewritten in form $g(x) = a(x - h)^2 + k$, where (h, k) is the vertex of the translated and scaled graph of f, with the scale factor of a, the leading coefficient. We can then quickly and efficiently (without the use of technology) sketch the graph of any quadratic function in the form $f(x) = a(x - h)^2 + k$ using transformations of the graph of the quadratic parent function, $f(x) = x^2$.

Problem Set

1. Write the function $g(x) = -2x^2 - 20x - 53$ in completed-square form. Describe the transformations of the graph of the parent function $f(x) = x^2$ that result in the graph of g.

2. Write the formula for the function whose graph is the graph of $f(x) = x^2$ translated 6.25 units to the right, vertically stretched by a factor of 8, and translated 2.5 units up.

3. Without using a graphing calculator, sketch the graphs of the functions below based on transformations of the graph of the parent function $f(x) = x^2$. Use your own graph paper, and label your graphs.

    a. $g(x) = (x + 2)^2 - 4$

    b. $h(x) = -(x - 4)^2 + 2$

    c. $k(x) = 2x^2 - 12x + 19$

    d. $p(x) = -2x^2 - 4x - 5$

    e. $q(x) = 3x^2 + 6x$

This page intentionally left blank

Lesson 22: Comparing Quadratic, Square Root, and Cube Root Functions Represented in Different Ways

Classwork

Opening Exercise

Populate the table on the right with values from the graph.

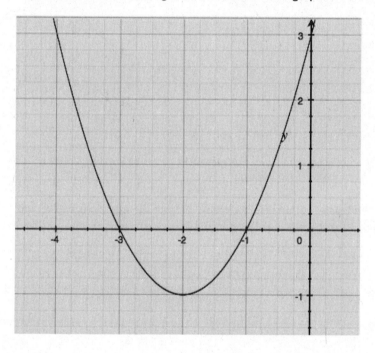

x	y

Exploratory Challenges 1–3

Solve each problem, and show or explain how you found your answers.

1. Xavier and Sherleese each threw a baseball straight up into the air. The relationship between the height (distance from the ground in feet) of Sherleese's ball with respect to the time since it was thrown, in seconds, is given by the function:

$$S(t) = -16t^2 + 79t + 6.$$

The graph of the height as a function of time of Xavier's ball is represented below.

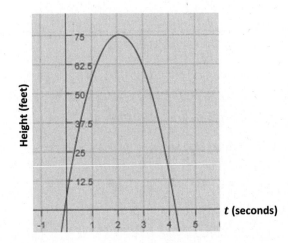

Xavier claims that his ball went higher than Sherleese's. Sherleese disagrees. Answer the questions below, and support your answers mathematically by comparing the features found in the equation to those in the graph.

a.   Who is right?

b.   For how long was each baseball airborne?

EUREKA
MATH™

c. Construct a graph of Sherleese's throw as a function of time (t) on the same set of axes as the graph of Xavier's, and use the graph to support your answers to parts (a) and (b).

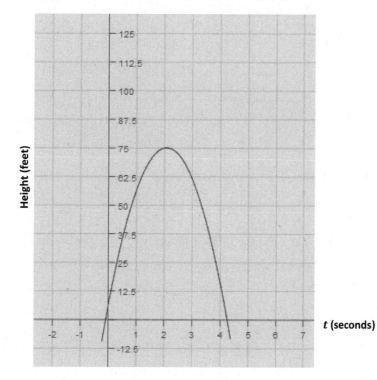

2. In science class, students constructed pendulums of various lengths and then recorded the time required for the pendulum to complete one full oscillation (out and back). The results are displayed in the table shown below.

a. Jack looks at the first three rows of the table and says that a linear function should be used to model the data. Based on the data, do you agree with him? Justify your reasoning.

Length (in cm)	Time (in seconds)
5	0.45
10	0.60
15	0.75
20	0.88
25	1.00
30	1.07
50	1.42
75	1.74
100	1.98

EUREKA
MATH™

Lesson 22:   Comparing Quadratic, Square Root, and Cube Root Functions
             Represented in Different Ways

S.133

©2015 Great Minds eureka-math.org
ALG I-M4-SE-B2-1.3.1-10.2015

b.   Create a scatterplot of length versus oscillation time.

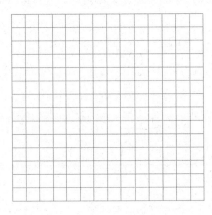

c.   Based on the scatterplot, what sort of function might be used to model the data?

d.   Mr. Williams, the science teacher, tells the students that the oscillation time for a pendulum can be found using the formula $T = 2\pi\sqrt{\dfrac{L}{9.8}}$ where L is the length of the pendulum, in meters, and T is the oscillation time, in seconds. Does this formula support the results from the table? Explain.

e.   Looking at the table of values, what effect does quadrupling the length of the pendulum have on the oscillation time? Use the formula from part (d) to demonstrate why this is the case.

EUREKA
MATH™

3. The growth of a Great Dane puppy can be represented by the graph below, where y represents the shoulder height (in inches) and x represents the puppy's age (in months).

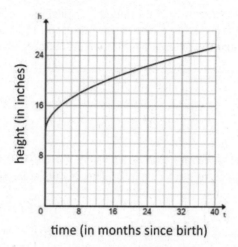

time (in months since birth)

The growth of a lion cub can be modeled by the function represented in the table below.

x (months since birth)	y (height in inches)
0	8
8	18
16	20.599
24	22.422
32	23.874

a. Which animal has the greater shoulder height at birth?

b. Which animal will have the greater shoulder height at 3 years of age (the age each animal is considered full-grown)?

c. If you were told that the domain for these functions is the set of all real numbers, would you agree? Why or why not?

Lesson Summary

The key features of a quadratic function, which are the zeros (roots), the vertex, and the leading coefficient, can be used to interpret the function in a context (e.g., the vertex represents the maximum or minimum value of the function). Graphing calculators and bivariate data tables are useful tools when comparing functions.

Problem Set

1. One type of rectangle has lengths that are always two inches more than their widths. The function f describes the relationship between the width of this rectangle in x inches and its area, $f(x)$, in square inches, and is represented in the table below.

x	$f(x)$
0	0
1	3
2	8
3	15
4	24
5	35

A second type of rectangle has lengths that are always one-half of their widths. The function $g(x) = \frac{1}{2}x^2$ describes the relationship between the width given in x inches and the area, $g(x)$, given in square inches of such a rectangle.

a. Use g to determine the area of a rectangle of the second type if the width is 20 inches.

b. Why is $(0,0)$ contained in the graphs of both functions? Explain the meaning of $(0,0)$ in terms of the situations that the functions describe.

c. Determine which function has a greater average rate of change on the interval $0 \leq x \leq 3$.

d. Interpret your answer to part (c) in terms of the situation being described.

e. Which type of rectangle has a greater area when the width is 5 inches? By how much?

f. Will the first type of rectangle always have a greater area than the second type of rectangle when widths are the same? Explain how you know.

Lesson 22: Comparing Quadratic, Square Root, and Cube Root Functions Represented in Different Ways

©2015 Great Minds eureka-math.org
ALG I-M4-SE-B2-1.3.1-10.2015

EUREKA MATH

2. The function given by the equation $y = \sqrt{x}$ gives the edge length, y units, of a square with area x square units. Similarly, the graph below describes the length of a leg, y units, of an isosceles right triangle whose area is x square units.

Graph of Isosceles Triangle Leg Lengths for Given Areas

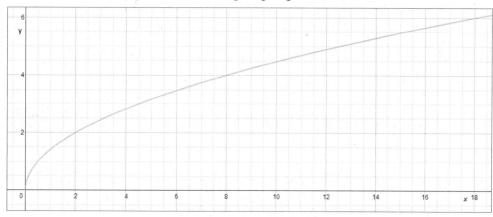

a. What is the length of a leg of an isosceles right triangle with an area of 12 square units?

b. Graph the function that represents a square with area x square units using the same graph that was given. Which function has a greater average rate of change on the interval $0 \le x \le 3$?

c. Interpret your answer to part (b) in terms of the situation being described.

d. Which will have a greater value: the edge length of a square with area 16 square units or the length of a leg of an isosceles right triangle with an area of 16 square units? Approximately by how much?

3. A portion of a graph of a cube root function, f, and select values of a square root function, g, are given below. The domain of g is $x \ge 0$.

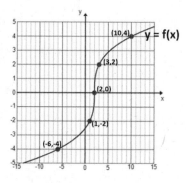

x	$g(x)$
0	3
1	3.5
4	4
9	4.5
16	5

Fill in each blank with one of the following: $>$, $<$, or $=$.

a. $f(2)$ _____ $g(2)$

b. y −intercept of f _____ y −intercept of g

c. Average rate of change of f on interval $[0,16]$ _____ Average rate of change of g on interval $[0,16]$

EUREKA MATH™   Lesson 22:   Comparing Quadratic, Square Root, and Cube Root Functions Represented in Different Ways   S.137

©2015 Great Minds eureka-math.org
ALG I-M4-SE-B2-1.3.1-10.2015

This page intentionally left blank

Lesson 23: Modeling with Quadratic Functions

Classwork

Opening: The Mathematics of Objects in Motion

Read the following explanation of the <u>Mathematics of Objects in Motion</u>:

Any object that is free falling or projected into the air without a power source is under the influence of gravity. All free-falling objects on Earth accelerate toward the center of Earth (downward) at a constant rate (-32 ft/s^2, or -9.8 m/s^2) because of the constant force of Earth's gravity (represented by g). That acceleration rate is included in the physics formula used for all objects in a free-falling motion. It represents the relationship of the height of the object (distance from Earth) with respect to the time that has passed since the launch or fall began. That formula is

$$h(t) = \tfrac{1}{2}gt^2 + v_0 t + h_0.$$

For this reason, the leading coefficient for a quadratic function that models the position of a falling, launched, or projected object must either be -16 or -4.9. Physicists use mathematics to make predictions about the outcome of a falling or projected object.

The mathematical formulas (equations) used in physics commonly use certain variables to indicate quantities that are most often used for motion problems. For example, the following are commonly used variables for an event that includes an object that has been dropped or thrown:

- h is often used to represent the function of height (how high the object is above earth in feet or meters);
- t is used to represent the time (number of seconds) that have passed in the event;
- v is used to represent *velocity* (the rate at which an object changes position in ft/s or m/s);
- s is used to represent the object's change in position, or *displacement* (how far the object has moved in feet or meters).

We often use subscripts with the variables, partly so that we can use the same variables multiple times in a problem without getting confused, but also to indicate the passage of time. For example:

- v_0 indicates the initial velocity (i.e., the velocity at 0 seconds);
- h_0 tells us the height of the object at 0 seconds, or the initial position.

So putting all of that together, we have a model representing the motion of falling or thrown objects, using U.S. standard units, as a quadratic function:

$$h(t) = -16t^2 + v_0 t + h_0,$$

where h represents the height of the object in feet (distance from Earth), and t is the number of seconds the object has been in motion. Note that the negative sign in front of the 16 (half of $g = 32$) indicates the downward pull of gravity. We are using a convention for quantities with direction here; upward is positive and downward is negative. If units are metric, the following equation is used:

$$h(t) = -4.9t^2 + v_0 t + h_0,$$

where everything else is the same, but now the height of the object is measured in meters and the velocity in meters per second.

These physics functions can be used to model many problems presented in the context of free-falling or projected objects (objects in motion without any inhibiting or propelling power source, such as a parachute or an engine).

Mathematical Modeling Exercise 1

Use the information in the Opening to answer the following questions.

Chris stands on the edge of a building at a height of 60 ft. and throws a ball upward with an initial velocity of 68 ft/s. The ball eventually falls all the way to the ground. What is the maximum height reached by the ball? After how many seconds will the ball reach its maximum height? How long will it take the ball to reach the ground?

 a. What units will we be using to solve this problem?

 b. What information from the contextual description do we need to use in the function equation?

 c. What is the maximum point reached by the ball? After how many seconds will it reach that height? Show your reasoning.

d.   How long will it take the ball to land on the ground after being thrown? Show your work.

e.   Graph the function of the height, h, of the ball in feet to the time , t, in seconds. Include and label key features of the graph such as the vertex, axis of symmetry, and t- and y-intercepts.

Mathematical Modeling Exercise 2

Read the following information about <u>Business Applications</u>:

Many business contexts can be modeled with quadratic functions. This is because the expressions representing the price (price per item), the cost (cost per item), and the quantity (number of items sold) are typically linear. The product of any two of those linear expressions will produce a quadratic expression that can be used as a model for the business context. The variables used in business applications are not as traditionally accepted as variables that are used in physics applications, but there are some obvious reasons to use c for cost, p for price, and q for quantity (all lowercase letters). For total production cost, we often use C for the variable, R for total revenue, and P for total profit (all uppercase letters). You have seen these formulas in previous lessons, but we will review them here since we use them in the next two lessons.

Business Application Vocabulary

UNIT PRICE (PRICE PER UNIT): The price per item a business sets to sell its product, sometimes represented as a linear expression.

QUANTITY: The number of items sold, sometimes represented as a linear expression.

REVENUE: The total income based on sales (but without considering the cost of doing business).

UNIT COST (COST PER UNIT) OR PRODUCTION COST: The cost of producing one item, sometimes represented as a linear expression.

PROFIT: The amount of money a business makes on the sale of its product. Profit is determined by taking the total revenue (the quantity sold multiplied by the price per unit) and subtracting the total cost to produce the items (the quantity sold multiplied by the production cost per unit): Profit = Total Revenue − Total Production Cost.

The following business formulas will be used in this lesson:

Total Production Costs = (cost per unit)(quantity of items sold)

Total Revenue = (price per unit)(quantity of items sold)

Profit = Total Revenue − Total Production Costs

Now answer the questions related to the following business problem:

A theater decided to sell special event tickets at \$10 per ticket to benefit a local charity. The theater can seat up to 1,000 people, and the manager of the theater expects to be able to sell all 1,000 seats for the event. To maximize the revenue for this event, a research company volunteered to do a survey to find out whether the price of the ticket could be increased without losing revenue. The results showed that for each \$1 increase in ticket price, 20 fewer tickets would be sold.

    a.   Let x represent the number of \$1.00 price-per-ticket increases. Write an expression to represent the expected price for each ticket.

b. Use the survey results to write an expression representing the possible number of tickets sold.

c. Using x as the number of $1-ticket price increases and the expression representing price per ticket, write the function, R, to represent the total revenue in terms of the number of $1-ticket price increases.

d. How many $1-ticket price increases will produce the maximum revenue? (In other words, what value for x produces the maximum R value?)

e. What is the price of the ticket that will provide the maximum revenue?

f. What is the maximum revenue?

EUREKA
MATH™

Lesson 23:   Modeling with Quadratic Functions

S.143

©2015 Great Minds eureka-math.org
ALG I-M4-SE-B2-1.3.1-10.2015

g. How many tickets will the theater sell to reach the maximum revenue?

h. How much more will the theater make for the charity by using the results of the survey to price the tickets than they would had they sold the tickets for their original $10 price?

Exercise 1

Two rock climbers try an experiment while scaling a steep rock face. They each carry rocks of similar size and shape up a rock face. One climbs to a point 400 ft. above the ground, and the other climbs to a place below her at 300 ft. above the ground. The higher climber drops her rock, and 1 second later, the lower climber drops his. *Note that the climbers are not vertically positioned. No climber is injured in this experiment.*

a. Define the variables in this situation, and write the two functions that can be used to model the relationship between the heights, h_1 and h_2, of the rocks, in feet, after t seconds.

©2015 Great Minds eureka-math.org
ALG I-M4-SE-B2-1.3.1-10.2015

b.   Assuming the rocks fall to the ground without hitting anything on the way, which of the two rocks will reach the ground last? Show your work, and explain how you know your answer is correct.

c.   Graph the two functions on the same coordinate plane, and identify the key features that show that your answer to part (b) is correct. Explain how the graphs show that the two rocks hit the ground at different times.

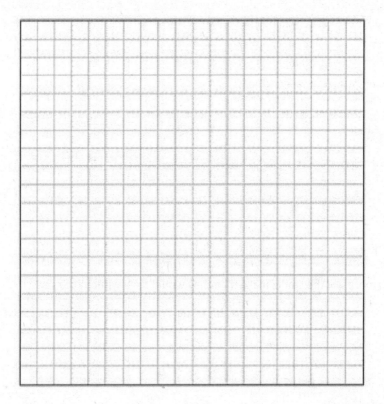

d. Does the graph show how far apart the rocks were when they landed? Explain.

Exercise 2

Amazing Photography Studio takes school pictures and charges $20 for each class picture. The company sells an average of 12 class pictures in each classroom. They would like to have a special sale that will help them sell more pictures and actually increase their revenue. They hired a business analyst to determine how to do that. The analyst determined that for every reduction of $2 in the cost of the class picture, there would be an additional 5 pictures sold per classroom.

a. Write a function to represent the revenue for each classroom for the special sale.

b. What should the special sale price be?

c. How much more will the studio make than they would have without the sale?

EUREKA
MATH™

Lesson Summary

We can write quadratic functions described verbally in a given context. We can also graph, interpret, analyze, or apply key features of quadratic functions to draw conclusions that help us answer questions taken from the problem's context.

- We find quadratic functions commonly applied in physics and business.
- We can substitute known x- and y-values into a quadratic function to create a linear system that, when solved, can identify the parameters of the quadratic equation representing the function.

Problem Set

1. Dave throws a ball upward with an initial velocity of 32 ft/s. The ball initially leaves his hand 5 ft. above the ground and eventually falls back to the ground. In parts (a)–(d), you will answer the following questions: What is the maximum height reached by the ball? After how many seconds will the ball reach its maximum height? How long will it take the ball to reach the ground?

   a. What units will we be using to solve this problem?

   b. What information from the contextual description do we need to use to write the formula for the function h of the height of the ball versus time? Write the formula for height of the ball in feet, $h(t)$, where t stands for seconds.

   c. What is the maximum point reached by the ball? After how many seconds will it reach that height? Show your reasoning.

   d. How long will it take for the ball to land on the ground after being thrown? Show your work.

   e. Graph the function of the height of the ball in feet to the time in seconds. Include and label key features of the graph such as the vertex, axis of symmetry, and t- and y-intercepts.

2. Katrina developed an app that she sells for $5 per download. She has free space on a website that will let her sell 500 downloads. According to some research she did, for each $1 increase in download price, 10 fewer apps are sold. Determine the price that will maximize her profit.

3. Edward is drawing rectangles such that the sum of the length and width is always six inches.

   a. Draw one of Edward's rectangles, and label the length and width.

   b. Fill in the following table with four different possible lengths and widths.

Width (inches)	Length (inches)

   c. Let x be the width. Write an expression to represent the length of one of Edward's rectangles.

   d. Write an equation that gives the area, y, in terms of the width, x.

   e. For what width and length will the rectangle have maximum area?

   f. Are you surprised by the answer to part (e)? What special name is given for the rectangle in your answer to part (e)?

4. Chase is standing at the base of a 60-foot cliff. He throws a rock in the air hoping to get the rock to the top of the cliff. If the rock leaves his hand 6 ft. above the base at a velocity of 80 ft/s, does the rock get high enough to reach the top of the cliff? How do you know? If so, how long does it take the rock to land on top of the cliff (assuming it lands on the cliff)? Graph the function and label the key features of the graph.

©2015 Great Minds eureka-math.org
ALG I-M4-SE-B2-1.3.1-10.2015

Lesson 24: Modeling with Quadratic Functions

Classwork

Opening Exercise

Draw as many quadratic graphs as possible through the following two points on the graph. Check with your neighbors for ideas. These points are (0,4) and (1,9).

Two Points

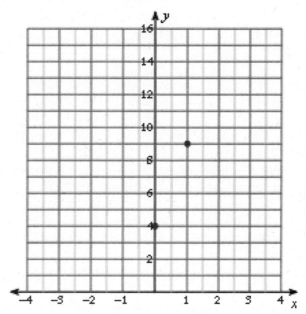

Example 1

Use the points $(0, 4)$, $(1, 9)$, and $(-3, 1)$ to write the equation for the quadratic function whose graph contains the three points.

EUREKA
MATH™

Exercise 1

Write in standard form the quadratic function defined by the points $(0,5)$, $(5,0)$, and $(3,-4)$.

Exercise 2

Louis dropped a watermelon from the roof of a tall building. As it was falling, Amanda and Martin were on the ground with a stopwatch. As Amanda called the seconds, Martin recorded the floor the watermelon was passing. They then measured the number of feet per floor and put the collected data into this table. Write a quadratic function to model the following table of data relating the height of the watermelon (distance in feet from the ground) to the number of seconds that had passed.

Height (distance from the ground) for a Watermelon That Was Dropped from a Tall Building					
Time (t)	0	1	2	3	4
Height $f(t)$	300	284	236	156	44

a. How do we know this data will be represented by a quadratic function?

b. Do we need to use all five data points to write the equation?

c. Are there any points that are particularly useful? Does it matter which we use? Write the quadratic function that models the data.

d. How does this equation for the function match up with what you learned about physics in Lesson 23? Is there a more efficient way to find this equation?

e. Can you use your quadratic function to predict at what time, t, the watermelon will hit the ground (i.e., $f(t) = 0$)?

EUREKA
MATH™

©2015 Great Minds eureka-math.org
ALG I-M4-SE-B2-1.3.1-10.2015

Lesson Summary

We can create a quadratic function from a data set based on a contextual situation, sketch its graph, and interpret both the function and the graph in context. We can then answer questions and make predictions related to the data, the quadratic function, and graph.

To determine a unique quadratic function from a table or graph, we must know at least three distinct points.

Problem Set

1. Write a quadratic function to fit the following points, and state the x-values for both roots. Then, sketch the graph to show that the equation includes the three points.

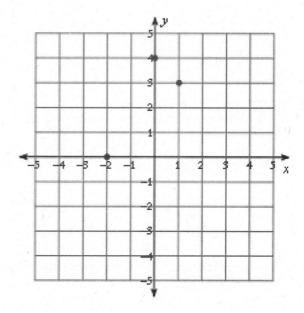

2. Write a quadratic function to fit the following points: $(0, 0.175), (20, 3.575), (30, 4.675)$.

This page intentionally left blank

Eureka Math
Algebra I
Module 5

Special thanks go to the Gordan A. Cain Center and to the Department of Mathematics at Louisiana State University for their support in the development of *Eureka Math*.

For a free *Eureka Math* Teacher Resource Pack, Parent Tip Sheets, and more please visit www.Eureka.tools

Printed in the U.S.A.

This book may be purchased from the publisher at eureka-math.org

10 9 8 7 6 5 4 3 2 1

ISBN 978-1-63255-325-6

Lesson 1: Analyzing a Graph

Classwork

Opening Exercise

The graphs below give examples for each parent function we have studied this year. For each graph, identify the function type and the general form of the parent function's equation; then offer general observations on the key features of the graph that helped you identify the function type. (Function types include linear, quadratic, exponential, square root, cube root, cubic, absolute value, and other piecewise functions. Key features may include the overall shape of the graph, x- and y-intercepts, symmetry, a vertex, end behavior, domain and range values or restrictions, and average rates of change over an interval.)

FUNCTION SUMMARY CHART		
Graph	**Function Type and Parent Function**	**Function Clues: Key Features, Observations**

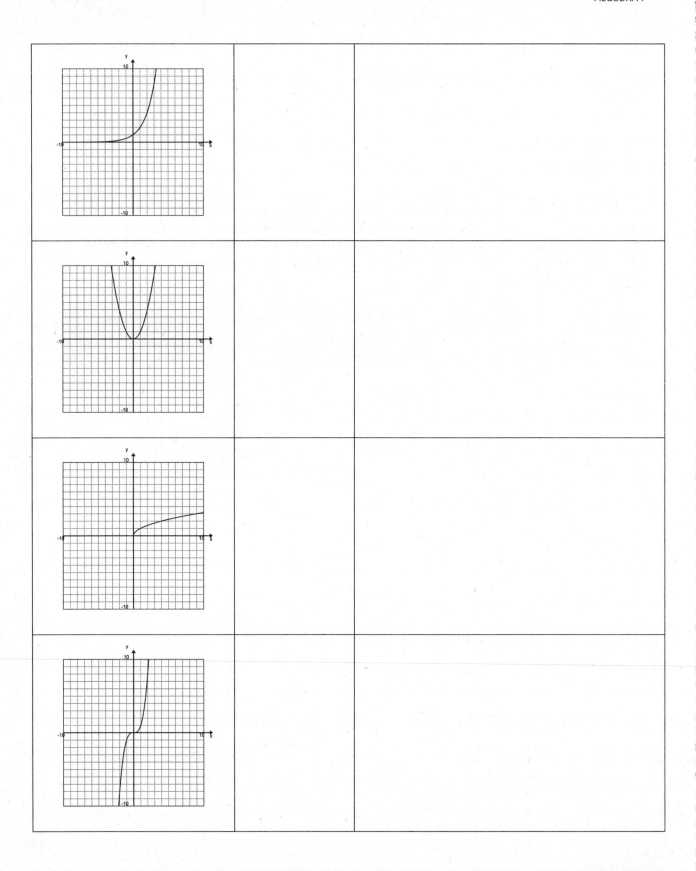

EUREKA
MATH™

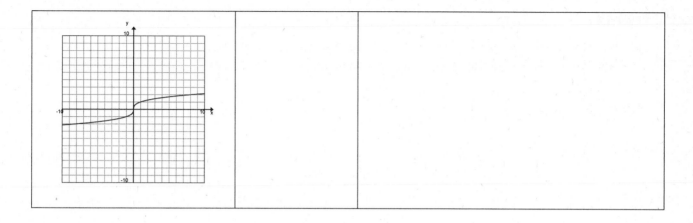

Example 1

Eduardo has a summer job that pays him a certain rate for the first 40 hours each week and time-and-a-half for any overtime hours. The graph below shows how much money he earns as a function of the hours he works in one week.

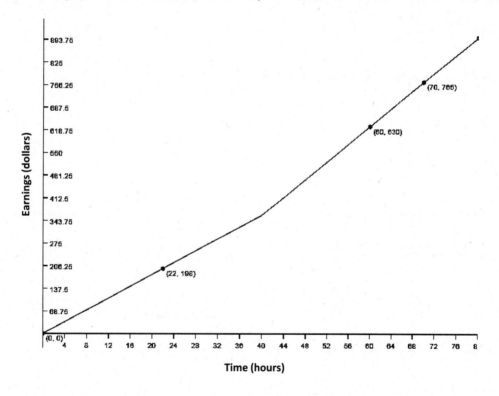

Exercises

1. Write the function in analytical (symbolic) form for the graph in Example 1.

   a. What is the equation for the first piece of the graph?

   b. What is the equation for the second piece of the graph?

   c. What are the domain restrictions for the context?

   d. Explain the domain in the context of the problem.

For each graph below use the questions and identified ordered pairs to help you formulate an equation to represent it.

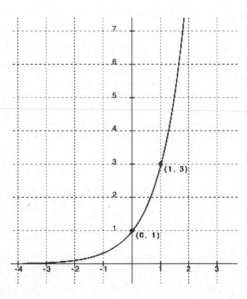

2. Function type:

   Parent function:

   Transformations:

   Equation:

EUREKA
MATH™

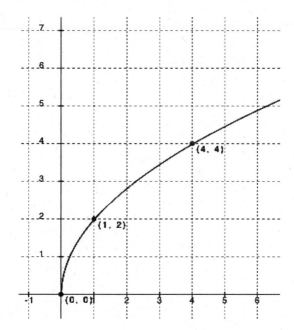

3. Function type:

    Parent function:

    Transformations:

    Equation:

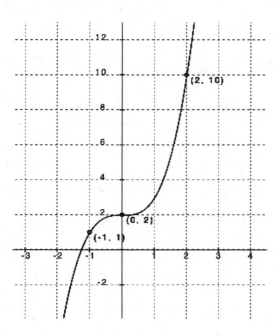

4. Function type:

    Parent function:

    Transformations:

    Equation:

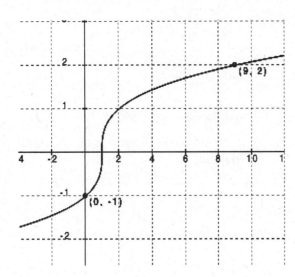

5. Function type:

   Parent function:

   Transformations:

   Equation:

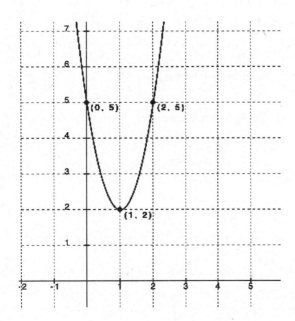

6. Function type:

   Parent function:

   Transformations:

   Equation:

EUREKA
MATH™

Lesson Summary

- When given a context represented graphically, you must first:
    - Identify the variables in the problem (dependent and independent), and
    - Identify the relationship between the variables that are described in the graph or situation.
- To come up with a modeling expression from a graph, you must recognize the type of function the graph represents, observe key features of the graph (including restrictions on the domain), identify the quantities and units involved, and create an equation to analyze the graphed function.
- Identifying a parent function and thinking of the transformation of the parent function to the graph of the function can help with creating the analytical representation of the function.

Problem Set

1. During tryouts for the track team, Bob is running 90-foot wind sprints by running from a starting line to the far wall of the gym and back. At time $t = 0$, he is at the starting line and ready to accelerate toward the opposite wall. As t approaches 6 seconds, he must slow down, stop for just an instant to touch the wall, turn around, and sprint back to the starting line. His distance, in feet, from the starting line with respect to the number of seconds that has passed for one repetition is modeled by the graph below.

    a. What are the key features of this graph?

    b. What are the units involved?

    c. What is the parent function of this graph?

    d. Were any transformations made to the parent function to get this graph?

    e. What general analytical representation would you expect to model this context?

    f. What do you already know about the parameters of the equation?

    g. Use the ordered pairs you know to replace the parameters in the general form of your equation with constants so that the equation will model this context. Check your answer using the graph.

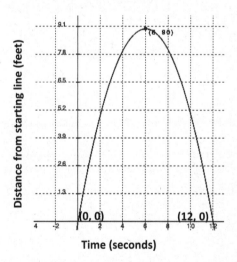

©2015 Great Minds eureka-math.org
ALG I-M5-SE-B2-1.3.1-10.2015

2. Spencer and McKenna are on a long-distance bicycle ride. Spencer leaves one hour before McKenna. The graph below shows each rider's distance in miles from his or her house as a function of time since McKenna left on her bicycle to catch up with Spencer. (Note: Parts (e), (f), and (g) are challenge problems.)

a. Which function represents Spencer's distance? Which function represents McKenna's distance? Explain your reasoning.

b. Estimate when McKenna catches up to Spencer. How far have they traveled at that point in time?

c. One rider is speeding up as time passes and the other one is slowing down. Which one is which, and how can you tell from the graphs?

d. According to the graphs, what type of function would best model each rider's distance?

e. Create a function to model each rider's distance as a function of the time since McKenna started riding her bicycle. Use the data points labeled on the graph to create a precise model for each rider's distance.

f. What is the meaning of the x- and y-intercepts of each rider in the context of this problem?

g. Estimate which rider is traveling faster 30 minutes after McKenna started riding. Show work to support your answer.

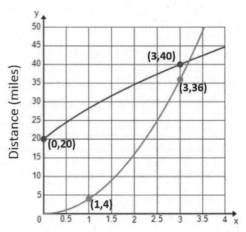

Time since McKenna left (hours)

Lesson 1:   Analyzing a Graph

©2015 Great Minds eureka-math.org
ALG I-M5-SE-B2-1.3.1-10.2015

EUREKA MATH

Lesson 2: Analyzing a Data Set

Classwork

Opening Exercise

When tables are used to model functions, we typically have just a few sample values of the function and therefore have to do some detective work to figure out what the function might be. Look at these three tables:

x	$f(x)$
0	6
1	12
2	18
3	24
4	30
5	36

x	$g(x)$
0	0
1	14
2	24
3	30
4	32
5	30

x	$h(x)$
0	1
1	3
2	9
3	27
4	81
5	243

Example 1

Noam and Athena had an argument about whether it would take longer to get from NYC to Boston and back by car or by train. To settle their differences, they made separate, nonstop round trips from NYC to Boston. On the trip, at the end of each hour, both recorded the number of miles they had traveled from their starting points in NYC. The tables below show their travel times, in hours, and the distances from their starting points, in miles. The first table shows Noam's travel time and distance from the starting point, and the second represents Athena's. Use both data sets to justify your answers to the questions below.

Time in Hours	Noam's Distance
0	0
1	55
2	110
3	165
4	220
5	165
6	110
7	55
8	0

Time in Hours	Athena's Distance
0	0
1	81
2	144
3	189
4	216
5	225
6	216
7	189
8	144
9	81
10	0

a.   Who do you think is driving, and who is riding the train? Explain your answer in the context of the problem.

b.   According to the data, how far apart are Boston and New York City? Explain mathematically.

EUREKA MATH™

c. How long did it take each of them to make the round trip?

d. According to their collected data, which method of travel was faster?

e. What was the average rate of change for Athena for the interval from 3 to 4 hours? How might you explain that in the context of the problem?

f. Noam believes a quadratic function can be used as a model for both data sets. Do you agree? Use and describe the key features of the functions represented by the data sets to support your answer.

Exercises

1. Explain why each function can or cannot be used to model the given data set.

   a. $f(x) = 3x + 5$

   b. $f(x) = -(x - 2)^2 + 9$

   c. $f(x) = -x^2 + 4x - 5$

x	$f(x)$
0	5
1	8
2	9
3	8
4	5
5	0
6	−7

   d. $f(x) = 3^x + 4$

   e. $f(x) = (x - 2)^2 + 9$

   f. $f(x) = -(x + 1)(x - 5)$

EUREKA MATH™

2.   Match each table below to the function and the context, and explain how you made your decision.

	A			B			C			D			E	
	x	y		x	y		x	y		x	y		x	y
	1	9		1	12		0	160		1	2		2	8
	2	18		2	24		1	174		2	4		3	9
	3	27		3	36		2	156		3	8		4	8
	4	18		4	48		3	106		4	16		5	5
	5	9		5	60		4	24		5	32		6	0

Equation ____   Equation ____   Equation ____   Equation ____   Equation ____

Context ____   Context ____   Context ____   Context ____   Context ____

Equations:

$f(x) = 12x$

$h(x) = -9|x - 3| + 27$

$g(x) = -(x)(x - 6)$

$p(x) = 2^x$

$q(x) = -16x^2 + 30x + 160$

Contexts:

1.   The population of bacteria doubled every month, and the total population vs. time was recorded.

2.   A ball was launched upward from the top of a building, and the vertical distance of the ball from the ground vs. time was recorded.

3.   The height of a certain animal's vertical leap was recorded at regular time intervals of one second; the animal returned to ground level after six seconds.

4.   Melvin saves the same amount of money every month. The total amount saved after each month was recorded.

5.   Chris ran at a constant rate on a straight-line path and then returned at the same rate. His distance from his starting point was recorded at regular time intervals.

Lesson Summary

The following methods can be used to determine the appropriate model for a given data set as a linear, quadratic, or exponential function:

- If the first difference is constant, then the data set could be modeled by a linear function.
- If the second difference is constant, then the data set could be modeled by a quadratic function.
- If the subsequent y-values are multiplied by a constant, then the data set could be modeled by an exponential function.

Problem Set

1.

x	y
0	
1	10
2	0
3	−6
4	−8
5	
6	

    a. Determine the function type that could be used to model the data set at the right and explain why.

    b. Complete the data set using the special pattern of the function you described above.

    c. If it exists, find the minimum or maximum value for the function model. If there is no minimum or maximum, explain why.

2.

x	y
−1	
0	
1	
2	16
3	64
4	256
5	1024

    a. Determine the function type that could be used to model the data set and explain why.

    b. Complete the data set using the special pattern of the function you described above.

    c. If it exists, find the minimum or maximum value for the function model. If there is no minimum or maximum, explain why.

3.

x	y
−1	
0	12
1	
2	24
3	
4	36
5	

    a. Determine the function type that could be used to model the data set and explain why.

    b. Complete the data set using the special pattern of the function you described above.

    c. If it exists, find the minimum or maximum value for the function model. If there is no minimum or maximum, explain why.

---

4. Circle all the function types that could possibly be used to model a context if the given statement applies.

a. When x-values are at regular intervals, the first difference of y-values is not constant.

| Linear Function | Quadratic Function | Exponential Function | Absolute Value Function |

b. When x-values are at regular intervals, the second difference of y-values is not constant.

| Linear Function | Quadratic Function | Exponential Function | Absolute Value Function |

c. When x-values are at regular intervals, the quotient of any two consecutive y-values is a constant that is not equal to 0 or 1.

| Linear Function | Quadratic Function | Exponential Function | Absolute Value Function |

d. There may be up to two different x-values for $y = 0$.

| Linear Function | Quadratic Function | Exponential Function | Absolute Value Function |

This page intentionally left blank

Lesson 3: Analyzing a Verbal Description

Classwork

Read the example problems below and discuss a problem-solving strategy with a partner or small group.

Example 1

Gregory plans to purchase a video game player. He has $500 in his savings account and plans to save $20 per week from his allowance until he has enough money to buy the player. He needs to figure out how long it will take. What type of function should he use to model this problem? Justify your answer mathematically.

Example 2

One of the highlights in a car show event is a car driving up a ramp and flying over approximately five cars placed end-to-end. The ramp is 8 ft at its highest point, and there is an upward speed of 88 ft/sec before it leaves the top of the ramp. What type of function can best model the height, h, in feet, of the car t seconds after leaving the end of the ramp? Justify your answer mathematically.

Example 3

Margie got $1,000 from her grandmother to start her college fund. She is opening a new savings account and finds out that her bank offers a 2% annual interest rate, compounded monthly. What type of function would best represent the amount of money in Margie's account? Justify your answer mathematically.

Exercises

1. City workers recorded the number of squirrels in a park over a period of time. At the first count, there were 15 pairs of male and female squirrels (30 squirrels total). After 6 months, the city workers recorded a total of 60 squirrels, and after a year, there were 120.

   a. What type of function can best model the population of squirrels recorded over a period of time, assuming the same growth rate and that no squirrel dies?

   b. Write a function that represents the population of squirrels recorded over x number of years. Explain how you determined your function.

2. A rectangular photograph measuring 8 in by 10 in is surrounded by a frame with a uniform width, x.

   a. What type of function can best represent the area of the picture and the frame in terms of x (the unknown frame's width)? Explain mathematically how you know.

   b. Write an equation in standard form representing the area of the picture and the frame. Explain how you arrive at your equation.

3. A ball is tossed up in the air at an initial rate of 50 ft/sec from 5 ft off the ground.

    a. What type of function models the height (h, in feet) of the ball after t seconds?

    b. Explain what is happening to the height of the ball as it travels over a period of time (in t seconds).

    c. What function models the height, h (in feet), of the ball over a period of time (in t seconds)?

4. A population of insects is known to triple in size every month. At the beginning of a scientific research project, there were 200 insects.

    a. What type of function models the population of the insects after t years?

    b. Write a function that models the population growth of the insects after t years.

Lesson Summary

The following methods can be used to recognize a function type from a word problem:

1. If a problem requires repeated addition or subtraction of a constant value, then it is represented by a linear function.
2. If a problem involves free-falling motion of an object or an area, then it is represented by a quadratic function.
3. If a problem is about population growth or compound interest, then it is represented by an exponential function.

Problem Set

1. The costs to purchase school spirit posters are as follows: two posters for $5, four posters for $9, six posters for $13, eight posters for $17, and so on.

    a. What type of function would best represent the cost of the total number of posters purchased?

    b. What function represents the cost of the total number of posters purchased? How did you know? Justify your reasoning.

    c. If you have $40 to spend, write an inequality to find the maximum number of posters you could buy.

2. NYC Sports Gym had 425 members in 2011. Based on statistics, the total number of memberships increases by 2% annually.

    a. What type of function models the total number of memberships in this situation?

    b. If the trend continues, what function represents the total number of memberships in n years? How did you know? Justify your reasoning.

3. Derek throws a baseball upward from an initial height of 3 ft. The baseball hits the ground after 2 seconds.

    a. What was the initial velocity of the baseball?

    b. What is the function that models the height, h (in feet), of the baseball over a period of time t (in seconds)?

    c. At what time did the baseball reach its maximum height? What was the maximum height of the baseball?

Lesson 3:   Analyzing a Verbal Description

Lesson 4: Modeling a Context from a Graph

Classwork

Example 1

Read the problem below. Your teacher will walk you through the process of using the steps in the modeling cycle to guide your solution.

The relationship between the length of one of the legs, in feet, of an animal and its walking speed, in feet per second, can be modeled by the graph below. Note: This function applies to walking not running speed. Obviously, a cheetah has shorter legs than a giraffe but can run much faster. However, in a walking race, the giraffe has the advantage.

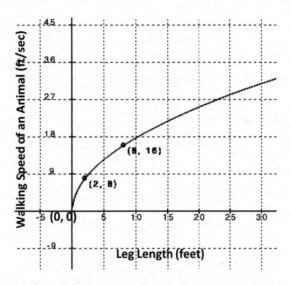

A T-Rex's leg length was 20 ft. What was the T-Rex's speed in ft/sec?

Exercises

Now practice using the modeling cycle with these problems:

1. Eduardo has a summer job that pays him a certain rate for the first 40 hours per week and time and a half for any overtime. The graph below is a representation of how much money he earns as a function of the hours he works in one week.

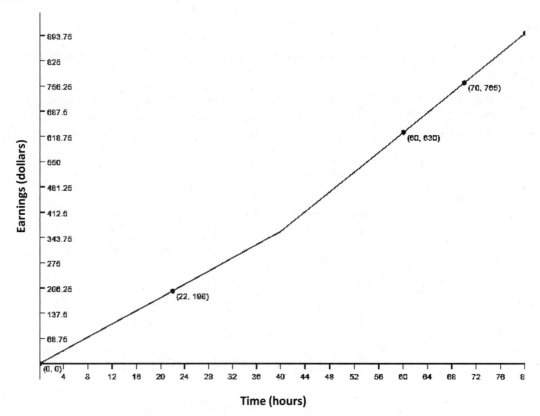

Eduardo's employers want to make him a salaried employee, which means he does not get overtime. If they want to pay him $480 per week but have him commit to 50 hours a week, should he agree to the salary change? Justify your answer mathematically.

a.   Formulate (recall this step from Lesson 1).

   i.   What type of function can be represented by a graph like this (e.g., quadratic, linear, exponential, piecewise, square root, or cube root)?

   ii.   How would you describe the end behavior of the graph in the context of this problem?

EUREKA
MATH™

©2015 Great Minds eureka-math.org
ALG I-M5-SE-B2-1.3.1-10.2015

iii.   How does this affect the equation of our function?

b.   Compute

i.   What strategy do you plan to use to come up with the model for this context?

ii.   Find the function of this graph. Show all your work.

c.   Interpret

i.   How much does Eduardo make an hour?

ii.   By looking only at the graphs, which interval has a greater average rate of change: $x < 20$, or $x > 45$? Justify your answer by making connections to the graph and its verbal description.

EUREKA
MATH™

Lesson 4:   Modeling a Context from a Graph

S.23

©2015 Great Minds eureka-math.org
ALG I-M5-SE-B2-1.3.1-10.2015

iii.   Eduardo's employers want to make Eduardo a salaried employee, which means he does not get overtime. If they want to pay him $480 per week but have him commit to 50 hours a week, should he agree to the salary change? Justify your answer mathematically.

d.   Validate

How can you check to make sure your function models the graph accurately?

2.   The cross-section view of a deep river gorge is modeled by the graph shown below where both height and distance are measured in miles. How long is a bridge that spans the gorge from the point labeled (1,0) to the other side? How high above the bottom of the gorge is the bridge?

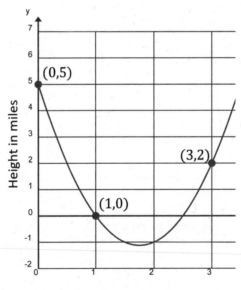

Distance in miles

a.   Formulate

i.   What type of function can be represented by a graph like this (e.g., quadratic, linear, exponential, piecewise, square root, or cube root)?

EUREKA
MATH™

ii.   What are the quantities in this problem?

iii. How would you describe the end behavior of the graph?

iv.   What is a general form for this function type?

v.   How does knowing the function type and end behavior affect the equation of the function for this graph?

vi.   What is the equation we would use to model this graph?

EUREKA
MATH™

Lesson 4:   Modeling a Context from a Graph

S.25

©2015 Great Minds eureka-math.org
ALG I-M5-SE-B2-1.3.1-10.2015

b. Compute

   i.   What are the key features of the graph that can be used to determine the equation?

   ii. Which key features of the function must be determined?

   iii. Calculate the missing key features and check for accuracy with your graph.

c. Interpret

   i.   What domain makes sense for this context? Explain.

   ii. How wide is the bridge with one side located at $(1,0)$?

   iii. How high is the bridge above the bottom of the gorge?

iv. Suppose the gorge is exactly 3.5 miles wide from its two highest points. Find the average rate of change for the interval from $x = 0$ to $x = 3.5$, $[0, 3.5]$. Explain this phenomenon. Are there other intervals that will behave similarly?

d. Validate

How can you check to make sure that your function models the graph accurately?

3. Now compare four representations that may be involved in the modeling process. How is each useful for each phase of the modeling cycle? Explain the advantages and disadvantages of each.

©2015 Great Minds eureka-math.org
ALG I-M5-SE-B2-1.3.1-10.2015

Lesson Summary

When modeling from a graph use the full modeling cycle:

- **FORMULATE:** Identify the variables involved, classify the type of graph presented, point out the visible key features, and create a different representation of the relationship if needed.

- **COMPUTE:** Decontextualize the graph from the application and analyze it. You might have to find a symbolic or tabular representation of the graph to further analyze it.

- **INTERPRET:** Contextualize the features of the function and your results and make sense of them in the context provided.

- **V** heck your results with the context. Do your answers make sense? Are the calculations accurate? Are there possibilities for error?

- **REPORT:** Clearly write your results.

Problem Set

1. During tryouts for the track team, Bob is running 90-foot wind sprints by running from a starting line to the far wall of the gym and back. At time $t = 0$, he is at the starting line and ready to accelerate toward the opposite wall. As t approaches 6 seconds, he must slow down, stop for just an instant to touch the wall, then turn around, and sprint back to the starting line. His distance, in feet, from the starting line with respect to the number of seconds that has passed for one repetition is modeled by the graph below.

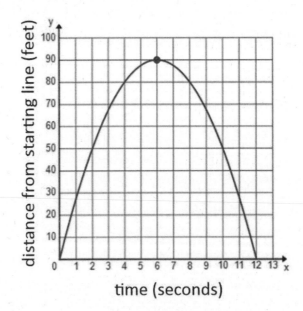

(Note: You may refer to Lesson 1, Problem Set #1 to help answer this question.)

How far was Bob from the starting line at 2 seconds? 6.5 seconds? (Distances, in feet, should be represented to the nearest tenth.)

2. Kyle and Abed each threw a baseball across a field. The height of the balls (in feet) is described by functions A and K, where t is the number of seconds the baseball is in the air. K models the height of Kyle's baseball (equation below), and A models the height of Abed's baseball (graph below).

$$K(t) = -16t^2 + 66t + 6.$$

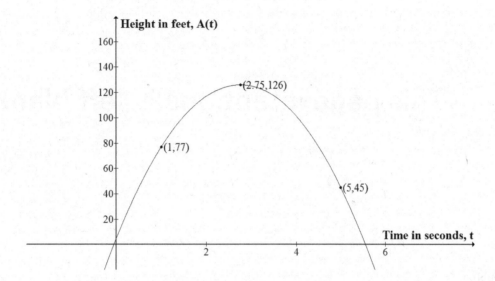

a. Which ball was in the air for a longer period of time?

b. Whose ball goes higher?

c. How high was Abed's ball when he threw it?

This page intentionally left blank

Lesson 5: Modeling from a Sequence

Classwork

Opening Exercise

A soccer coach is getting her students ready for the season by introducing them to High Intensity Interval Training (HIIT). She presents the table below with a list of exercises for a HIIT training circuit and the length of time that must be spent on each exercise before the athlete gets a short time to rest. The rest times increase as students complete more exercises in the circuit. Study the chart and answer the questions below. How long would the tenth exercise be? If a player had 30 minutes of actual gym time during a period, how many exercises could she get done? Explain your answers.

Exercise Number	Length of Exercise Time	Length of Rest Time
Exercise 1	0.5 minutes	0.25 minutes
Exercise 2	0.75 minutes	0.5 minutes
Exercise 3	1 minute	1 minutes
Exercise 4	1.25 minutes	2 minutes
Exercise 5	1.5 minutes	4 minutes

Example 1

Determine whether the sequence below is arithmetic or geometric, and find the function that will produce any given term in the sequence:

$$16, 24, 36, 54, 81, \ldots$$

Is this sequence arithmetic?

Is the sequence geometric?

What is the analytical representation of the sequence?

Exercises

Look at the sequence and determine the analytical representation of the sequence. Show your work and reasoning.

1. A decorating consultant charges $50 for the first hour and $2 for each additional whole hour. How much would 1,000 hours of consultation cost?

n	1	2	3	4	5	...	n
$f(n)$	50	52	54	56	58		?

EUREKA
MATH

©2015 Great Minds eureka-math.org
ALG I-M5-SE-B2-1.3.1-10.2015

2. The sequence below represents the area of a square whose side length is the diagonal of a square with integer side length n. What would be the area for the 100th square? Hint: You can use the square below to find the function model, but you can also just use the terms of the sequence.

n	1	2	3	4	5	...	n
$f(n)$	2	8	18	32	50		?

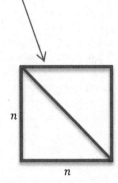

3. What would be the tenth term in the sequence?

n	1	2	3	4	...	n
$f(n)$	3	6	12	24		?

Lesson Summary

- A sequence is a list of numbers or objects in a special order.

- An arithmetic sequence goes from one term to the next by adding (or subtracting) the same value.

- A geometric sequence goes from one term to the next by multiplying (or dividing) by the same value.

- Looking at the difference of differences can be a quick way to determine if a sequence can be represented as a quadratic expression.

Problem Set

Solve the following problems by finding the function/formula that represents the nth term of the sequence.

1. After a knee injury, a jogger is told he can jog 10 minutes every day and that he can increase his jogging time by 2 minutes every two weeks. How long will it take for him to be able to jog one hour a day?

Week #	Daily Jog Time
1	10
2	10
3	12
4	12
5	14
6	14

2. A ball is dropped from a height of 10 feet. The ball then bounces to 80% of its previous height with each subsequent bounce.

   a. Explain how this situation can be modeled with a sequence.

   b. How high (*to the nearest tenth of a foot*) does the ball bounce on the fifth bounce?

3. Consider the following sequence:

$$8, 17, 32, 53, 80, 113, \dots$$

   a. What pattern do you see, and what does that pattern mean for the analytical representation of the function?

   b. What is the symbolic representation of the sequence?

4. Arnold wants to be able to complete 100 military-style pull-ups. His trainer puts him on a workout regimen designed to improve his pull-up strength. The following chart shows how many pull-ups Arnold can complete after each month of training. How many months will it take Arnold to achieve his goal if this pattern continues?

Month	Pull-Up Count
1	2
2	5
3	10
4	17
5	26
6	37
...	

Lesson 5:   Modeling from a Sequence

EUREKA MATH

©2015 Great Minds eureka-math.org
ALG I-M5-SE-B2-1.3.1-10.2015

Lesson 6: Modeling a Context from Data

Classwork

Opening Exercise

a. Identify the type of function that each table appears to represent (e.g., quadratic, linear, exponential, square root).

A		B		C	
x	y	x	y	x	y
1	5	1	6	1	3
2	7	2	9	2	12
3	9	3	13.5	3	27
4	11	4	20.25	4	48
5	13	5	30.375	5	75

b. Explain how you were able to identify the function.

c. Find the symbolic representation of the function.

d. Plot the graphs of your data.

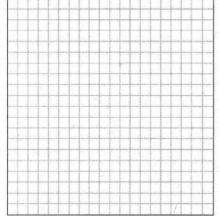 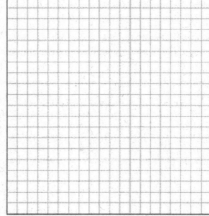 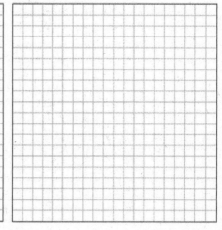

Example 1

Enrique is a biologist who has been monitoring the population of a rare fish in Lake Placid. He has tracked the population for 5 years and has come up with the following estimates:

Year Tracked	Year Since 2002	Estimated Fish Population
2002	0	1,000
2003	1	899
2004	2	796
2005	3	691
2006	4	584

Create a graph and a function to model this situation, and use it to predict (assuming the trend continues) when the fish population will be gone from the Lake Placid ecosystem. Verify your results, and explain the limitations of each model.

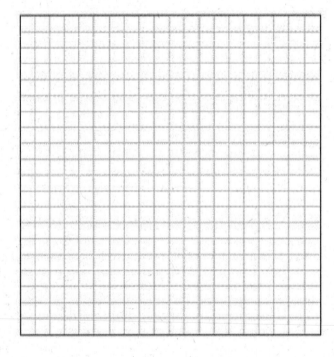

Lesson 6:   Modeling a Context from Data

©2015 Great Minds eureka-math.org
ALG I-M5-SE-B2-1.3.1-10.2015

EUREKA
MATH™

Exercises

1. Bella is a BMX bike racer and wants to identify the relationship between her bike's weight and the height of jumps (a category she gets judged on when racing). On a practice course, she tests out 7 bike models with different weights and comes up with the following data.

Weight (lb)	Height of Jump (ft)
20	8.9
21	8.82
22	8.74
23	8.66
24	8.58
25	8.5
26	8.42
27	8.34

   a. Bella is sponsored by Twilight Bikes and must ride a 32 lb bike. What can she expect her jump height to be?

   b. Bella asks the bike engineers at Twilight to make the lightest bike possible. They tell her the lightest functional bike they could make is 10 lb. Based on this data, what is the highest she should expect to jump if she only uses Twilight bikes?

   c. What is the maximum weight of a bike if Bella's jumps have to be at least 2 ft high during a race?

EUREKA
MATH™

Lesson 6:   Modeling a Context from Data

S.37

©2015 Great Minds eureka-math.org
ALG I-M5-SE-B2-1.3.1-10.2015

2. The concentration of medicine in a patient's blood as time passes is recorded in the table below.

Time (hours)	Concentration of Medicine (ml)
0	0
0.5	55.5
1	83
1.5	82.5
2	54

a. The patient cannot be active while the medicine is in his blood. How long, to the nearest minute, must the patient remain inactive? What are the limitations of your model(s)?

b. What is the highest concentration of medicine in the patient's blood?

3. A student is conducting an experiment, and as time passes, the number of cells in the experiment decreases. How many cells will there be after 16 minutes?

Time (minutes)	Cells
0	5,000,000
1	2,750,000
2	1,512,500
3	831,875
4	457,531
5	251,642
6	138,403

Lesson Summary

When given a data set, strategies that could be used to determine the type of function that describes the relationship between the data are

- Determine the variables involved and plot the points.
- After making sure the x-values are given at regular intervals, look for common differences between the data points—first and second.
- Determine the type of sequence the data models first, and then use the general form of the function equation to find the parameters for the symbolic representation of the function.

Problem Set

Research linear, quadratic, and exponential functions using the Internet. For each of the three types of functions, provide an example of a problem/situation you found on the Internet where that function was used to model the situation or answer the problem. Include the actual function used in the example and web page where you found the example.

EUREKA
MATH™

Lesson 7: Modeling a Context from Data

Classwork

Opening Exercise

What is this data table telling us?

Age (Years)	NYC Marathon Running Time (Minutes)
15	300
25	190
35	180
45	200
55	225
65	280

Example 1

Remember that in Module 2, we used a graphing display calculator (GDC) to find a linear regression model. If a linear model is not appropriate for a collection of data, it may be possible that a quadratic or exponential model will be a better fit. Your graphing calculator is capable of determining various types of regressions. Use a GDC to determine if a data set has a better fit with a quadratic or exponential function. You may need to review entering the data into the stats application of your GDC.

When you are ready to begin, return to the data presented in the Opening Exercise. Use your graphing calculator to determine the function that best fits the data. Then, answer some questions your teacher will ask about the data.

Exercises

1. Use the following data table to construct a regression model, and then answer the questions.

Chicken Breast Frying Time (Minutes)	Moisture Content (%)
5	16.3
10	9.7
15	8.1
20	4.2
25	3.4
30	2.9
45	1.9
60	1.3

Data Source: *Journal of Food Processing and Preservation*, 1995

a. What function type appears to be the best fit for this data? Explain how you know.

b. A student chooses a quadratic regression to model this data. Is he right or wrong? Why or why not?

c. Will the moisture content for this product ever reach 0%? Why or why not?

d. Based on this model, what would you expect the moisture content to be of a chicken breast fried for 50 minutes?

©2015 Great Minds eureka-math.org
ALG I-M5-SE-B2-1.3.1-10.2015

2. Use the following data table to construct a regression model, then answer the questions based on your model.

Prevalence of No Leisure-Time Activities, 1988 - 2008

Year	Years since 1988	% of prevalence
1988	0	30.5
1989	1	31.5
1990	2	30.9
1991	3	30.6
1992	4	29.3
1994	6	30.2
1996	8	28.4
1998	10	28.4
2000	12	27.8
2001	13	26.2
2002	14	25.1
2003	15	24.2
2004	16	23.7
2005	17	25.1
2006	18	23.9
2007	19	23.9
2008	20	25.1

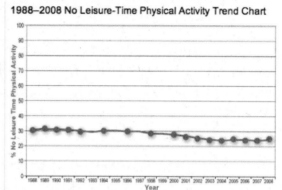

1988–2008 No Leisure-Time Physical Activity Trend Chart

a. What trends do you see in this collection of data?

b. How do you interpret this trend?

c. If the trend continues, what would we expect the percentage of people in the U.S. who report no leisure-time physical activity to be in 2020?

Lesson Summary

- Using data plots and other visual displays of data, the function type that appears to be the best fit for the data can be determined. Using the correlation coefficient, the measure of the strength and the direction of a linear relationship can be determined.

- A graphing calculator can be used if the data sets are imperfect. To find a regression equation, the same steps will be performed as for a linear regression.

Problem Set

1. Use the following data tables to write a regression model, and then answer the questions:

Prescription Drug Sales in the United States Since 1995

Years Since 1995	Prescription Drug Sales (billions of USD)
0	68.6
2	81.9
3	103.0
4	121.7
5	140.7

a. What is the best model for this data?

b. Based on your model, what were prescription drug sales in 2002? 2005?

c. For this model, would it make sense to input negative values for t into your regression? Why or why not?

2. Use the data below to answer the questions that follow:

Per Capita Ready-to-Eat Cereal Consumption in the United States per Year Since 1980

Years Since 1980	Cereal Consumption (lb.)	Years Since 1980	Cereal Consumption (lb.)
0	12	10	15.4
1	12	11	16.1
2	11.9	12	16.6
3	12.2	13	17.3
4	12.5	14	17.4
5	12.8	15	17.1
6	13.1	16	16.6
7	13.3	17	16.3
8	14.2	18	15.6
9	14.9	19	15.5

a. What is the best model for this data?

b. Based on your model, what would you expect per capita cereal consumption in 2002? 2005?

c. For this model, will it make sense to input t-values that return negative output values? Why or why not?

Lesson 8: Modeling a Context from a Verbal Description

Classwork

Example 1

Christine has $500 to deposit in a savings account, and she is trying to decide between two banks. Bank A offers 10% annual interest compounded quarterly. Rather than compounding interest for smaller accounts, Bank B offers to add $15 quarterly to any account with a balance of less than $1,000 for every quarter, as long as there are no withdrawals. Christine has decided that she will neither withdraw, nor make a deposit for a number of years.

Develop a model that will help Christine decide which bank to use.

Example 2

Alex designed a new snowboard. He wants to market it and make a profit. The total initial cost for manufacturing set-up, advertising, etc. is $500,000, and the materials to make the snowboards cost $100 per board.

The demand function for selling a similar snowboard is $D(p) = 50,000 - 100p$, where p represents the selling price (in dollars) of each snowboard.

   a.   Write an expression for each of the following in terms of p.

   Demand Function (number of units that will sell)

   Revenue [(number of units that will sell)(price per unit, p)]

   Total Cost (cost for producing the snowboards)

b. Write an expression to represent the profit.

c. What is the selling price of the snowboard that will give the maximum profit?

d. What is the maximum profit Alex can make?

Exercises

Alvin just turned 16 years old. His grandmother told him that she will give him $10,000 to buy any car he wants whenever he is ready. Alvin wants to be able to buy his dream car by his 21st birthday, and he wants a 2009 Avatar Z, which he could purchase today for $25,000. The car depreciates (reduces in value) at a rate is 15% per year. He wants to figure out how long it would take for his $10,000 to be enough to buy the car, without investing the $10,000.

1. Write the function that models the depreciated value of the car after n number of years.

After n years	Value of the Car
1	
2	
3	
4	
5	
6	

a. Will he be able to afford to buy the car when he turns 21? Explain why or why not.

b. Given the same rate of depreciation, after how many years will the value of the car be less than $5,000?

EUREKA
MATH™

©2015 Great Minds eureka-math.org
ALG I-M5-SE-B2-1.3.1-10.2015

c. If the same rate of depreciation were to continue indefinitely, after how many years would the value of the car be approximately $1?

2. Sophia plans to invest $1,000 in each of three banks.

Bank A offers an annual interest rate of 12%, compounded annually.

Bank B offers an annual interest rate of 12%, compounded quarterly.

Bank C offers an annual interest rate of 12%, compounded monthly.

a. Write the function that describes the growth of investment for each bank in n years.

b. How many years will it take to double her initial investment for each bank? (Round to the nearest whole dollar.)

Year	Bank A	Bank B	Bank C
Year 1			
Year 2			
Year 3			
Year 4			
Year 5			
Year 6			
Year 7			

c. Sophia went to Bank D. The bank offers a "double your money" program for an initial investment of $1,000 in five years, compounded annually. What is the annual interest rate for Bank D?

Lesson Summary

- We can use the full modeling cycle to solve real-world problems in the context of business and commerce (e.g., compound interest, revenue, profit, and cost) and population growth and decay (e.g., population growth, depreciation value, and half-life) to demonstrate linear, exponential, and quadratic functions described verbally through using graphs, tables, or algebraic expressions to make appropriate interpretations and decisions.

- Sometimes a graph or table is the best model for problems that involve complicated function equations.

Problem Set

1. Maria invested $10,000 in the stock market. Unfortunately, the value of her investment has been dropping at an average rate of 3% each year.

    a. Write the function that best models the situation.

    b. If the trend continues, how much will her investment be worth in 5 years?

    c. Given the situation, what should she do with her investment?

2. The half-life of the radioactive material in Z-Med, a medication used for certain types of therapy, is 2 days. A patient receives a 16 mCi dose (millicuries, a measure of radiation) in his treatment. (*Half-life* means that the radioactive material decays to the point where only half is left.)

    a. Make a table to show the level of Z-Med in the patient's body after n days.

Number of Days	Level of Z-Med in Patient
0	
2	
4	
6	
8	
10	

    b. Write a formula to model the half-life of Z-Med for n days. (Be careful here. Make sure that the formula works for both odd and even numbers of days.)

    c. How much radioactive material from Z-Med is left in the patient's body after 20 days of receiving the medicine?

3. Suppose a male and a female of a certain species of animal were taken to a deserted island. The population of this species quadruples (multiplies by 4) every year. Assume that the animals have an abundant food supply and that there are no predators on the island.

    a.   What is an equation that can be used to model the population of the species?

    b.   What will the population of the species be after 5 years?

After n years	Population
0	
1	
2	
3	
4	
5	

    c.   Write an equation to find how many years it will take for the population of the animals to exceed 1 million. Find the number of years, either by using the equation or a table.

After n years	Population
0	
1	
2	
3	
4	
5	
6	
7	
8	
9	
10	

4. The revenue of a company for a given month is represented as $R(x) = 1,500x - x^2$ and its costs as $C(x) = 1,500 + 1,000x$. What is the selling price, x, of its product that would yield the maximum profit? Show or explain your answer.

This page intentionally left blank

Lesson 9: Modeling a Context from a Verbal Description

Classwork

Opening Exercise

What does it mean to attend to precision when modeling in mathematics?

Example 1

Marymount Township secured the construction of a power plant, which opened in 1990. Once the power plant opened in 1990, the population of Marymount increased by about 20% each year for the first ten years and then increased by 5% each year after that.

   a.   If the population was 150,000 people in 2010, what was the population in 2000?

   b.   How should you round your answer? Explain.

   c.   What was the population in 1990?

Example 2

If the trend continued, what would the population be in 2009?

Exercises

1. A tortoise and a hare are having a race. The tortoise moves at 4 miles per hour. The hare travels at 10 miles per hour. Halfway through the race, the hare decides to take a 5-hour nap and then gets up and continues at 10 miles per hour.

    a. If the race is 40 miles long, who won the race? Support your answer with mathematical evidence.

    b. How long (in miles) would the race have to be for there to be a tie between the two creatures, if the same situation (as described in Exercise 1) happened?

©2015 Great Minds eureka-math.org
ALG I-M5-SE-B2-1.3.1-10.2015

2. The graph on the right represents the value V of a popular stock. Its initial value was \$12/share on day 0.

   Note: The calculator uses X to represent t, and Y to represent V.

   a. How many days after its initial value at time $t = 0$ did the stock price return to \$12 per share?

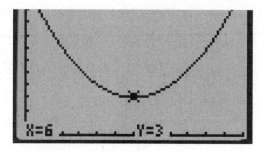

   b. Write a quadratic equation representing the value of this stock over time.

   c. Use this quadratic equation to predict the stock's value after 15 days.

Lesson Summary

The full modeling cycle is used to interpret the function and its graph, compute for the rate of change over an interval, and attend to precision to solve real-world problems in the context of population growth and decay and other problems in geometric sequences or forms of linear, exponential, and quadratic functions.

Problem Set

1. According to the Center for Disease Control and Prevention, the breast cancer rate for women has decreased at 0.9% per year between 2000 and 2009.

    a. If 192,370 women were diagnosed with invasive breast cancer in 2009, how many were diagnosed in 2005? For this problem, assume that there is no change in population from 2005 and 2009.

    b. According to the American Cancer Society, in 2005 there were 211,240 people diagnosed with breast cancer. In a written response, communicate how precise and accurate your solution in part (a) is, and explain why.

2. The functions f and g represent the population of two different kinds of bacteria, where x is the time (in hours) and f and g are the number of bacteria (in thousands). $f(x) = 2x^2 + 7$ and $g(x) = 2^x$.

    a. Between the third and sixth hour, which bacteria had a faster rate of growth?

    b. Will the population of g ever exceed the population of f? If so, at what hour?

©2015 Great Minds eureka-math.org
ALG I-M5-SE-B2-1.3.1-10.2015